You welcomed me
Interfaith spiritual care in the hospital

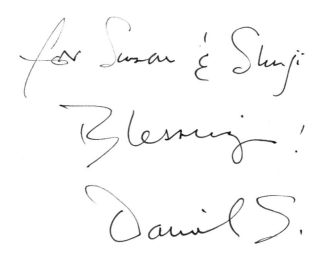

for Susan & Shinji

Blessings!

Daniel S.

You welcomed me
Interfaith spiritual care in the hospital

Leah Dawn Bueckert and
Daniel S. Schipani, editors

PANDORA
PRESS
Kitchener, Ontario

You welcomed me
Interfaith spiritual care in the hospital

Published by Pandora Press
33 Kent Avenue
Kitchener, Ontario N2G 3R2
Toll Free: 866.696.1678
Web site: www.pandorapress.com

Book design by Mary E. Klassen

Cover illustration: Reprinted from *Clip Art for Year A* by Steve Erspamer, SM ©1992, Archdiocese of Chicago: Liturgy Training Publications, 1800 North Hermitage Avenue, Chicago, IL 60622. www.lpt.org.

All Pandora Press books are printed on Eco-Logo certified paper.

Unless otherwise indicated, the scripture quotations in this book are from the New Revised Standard Version of the Bible, copyright © 1989 by the Division of Christian Education of the National Council of Churches of Christ in the USA, and are used by permission.

Library and Archives Canada Cataloguing in Publication

You welcomed me: interfaith spiritual care in the hospital / edited by Leah Dawn Bueckert and Daniel S. Schipani.

Includes bibliographical references.
ISBN 978-1-926599-14-4

1. Chaplains, Hospital. 2. Spiritual care (Medical care). 3. Church work with the sick. I. Schipani, Daniel S. II. Bueckert, Leah Dawn

BV4335.Y68 2010   259'.411   C2010-905578-0

Contents

Preface

I was a stranger and you welcomed me...I was sick and you took care of me...

Truly I tell you, just as you did it to one of the least of these
who are members of my family, you did it to me.
Matthew 25:35-36

Jesus' words quoted above suggest a way to set the tone for our discussion: interfaith spiritual care is a special occasion for welcoming and taking care of the sick regardless of their social, religious, or spiritual condition. The intended connotations of the phrase chosen for the title of this book—"you welcomed me"—assume three different subjects. First of all, according to the parable,[1] Jesus himself is vicariously welcomed and taken care of whenever the "righteous" welcome those strangers and visit and take care of the sick who happen to be "members of his family."[2] Second, it is clear that the care receivers must be welcomed and cared for while they experience the institutional strangeness of the hospital setting which becomes part of the health and life crisis they are confronting. Finally, the caregivers who visit and take care of the sick strangers must themselves experience being welcomed and somehow cared for by those very care seekers if their ministry is going to be fruitful at all.

[1] Given the textual setting of the parable in the Gospel of Matthew, chapter 25, where we find colorful metaphorical stories alluding to judgment, the text that includes the sentence, "you welcomed me," might be considered as an *eschatological* parable.

[2] There has been considerable debate regarding who the "righteous" and the "members of Jesus' family" actually are. Matthew's judgment scene in 21:31-46 is the culmination of a two-chapter eschatological discourse, and it has been interpreted in diverse ways. In any event, two things should be kept in mind. First, for Matthew Jesus is identified with the (marginalized) community of disciples, and he is present with them as they engage in mission to communicate the gospel (18:20; 28:20). Second, in this text Jesus praises the actions of the righteous from "all nations" (presumably Gentiles as well as Jews) because they have lived out the gospel by caring for the poor, oppressed, and marginalized; the actions of these "sheep" blessed by the Father are the practices of service expected of gospel bearers, followers of Jesus Christ. See, Warren Carter, *Matthew and the Margins: A Sociopolitical and Religious Reading* (Maryknoll: Orbis Books, 2000), pp. 491-496.

In light of the agenda we have set for ourselves, the parable suggests that care receivers and caregivers can actually mediate the Spirit of Christ to each other. Christian pastoral caregivers are vocationally committed to care well in the name and in the manner of Jesus, especially when encountering the sick among strangers of other faiths. At the same time, Christian caregivers can expect to encounter Christ anew in the midst of such a relationship. In other words, thus welcoming and caring becomes not only an occasion for healing but also a place of grace and epiphany. Interestingly enough, the parable also teaches that making verbally or consciously explicit the connection with Jesus Christ is not essential ("Lord, when was it that we saw you ...?" v. 38-39)! Rather, it is the practice of unconditional, indiscriminate love in compassionately welcoming strangers and taking care of the sick that is essential.

This book furthers the pastoral theological reflection presented in our previous work, *Spiritual Caregiving in the Hospital: Windows to Chaplaincy Ministry*.[3] It is fitting, then, to paraphrase the very last words in that book, which serve as a twofold guiding principle for understanding and practicing interfaith spiritual care: on the one hand we affirm the essential place of clinical and professional competence; on the other hand, in light of our theological convictions, we claim that, ultimately, the source of all healing and life-giving transformation is not the excellence of our ministry but the Spirit of grace and wisdom with whom we are partners.[4]

An earlier version of the present volume stemmed from a year-long seminar originally sponsored by the Lutheran Hospital of Indiana (LHI) Pastoral Care Division and Associated Mennonite Biblica Seminary (AMBS) Pastoral Care and Counseling Program. Our collaboration provided a unique opportunity to reflect systematically on pastoral care in interfaith situations in the hospital setting.[5] The records of our work together include a wealth of material which has been presented, discussed and expanded in numerous workshops and in several international conferences in Canada (Canadian Association for Spiritual Care), the United

---

[3] We discuss the art of language care to facilitate interfaith communication in pastoral care in, Leah Dawn Bueckert and Daniel S. Schipani, "Interfaith Spiritual Caregiving: The Case for Language Care," Leah Dawn Bueckert and Daniel S. Schipani, eds. *Spiritual Caregiving in the Hospital: Windows to Chaplaincy Ministry* (Kitchener: Pandora Press, 2006), pp. 245-263.

[4] Ibid., 263.

[5] The original study, for which Lutheran Hospital of Indiana served as the main hosting clinical setting, took place from September 2006 to August 2007. Seminar-style meetings consisted in the presentation and systematic discussion of interfaith care situations. Appendix I includes standards and codes of ethics with indispensable material for the normative framework of the professional and academic endeavors related to interfaith spiritual care. Appendix II presents a tool for spiritual assessment and another one for pastoral theological reflection on spiritual care situations.

States and Europe (International Academy of Practical Theology, Society for Intercultural Pastoral Care and Counseling).

This book is therefore a contribution to our pastoral care and Clinical Pastoral Education colleagues and students in the field. It is presented as a testimony regarding the integration of theology and church ministry with the practical and clinical wisdom of spiritual caregivers within the hospital setting.

Gratitudes

We are grateful for the many ways in which the AMBS and the Pastoral Care Division of LHI supported the original research and writing project partially documented in this book. Special thanks go to two wonderful partners at LHI whose collaborative spirit and competence as pastoral caregivers, supervisors, and pastoral theologians, contributed to make the project a successful and enjoyable endeavor: John D. Peterson, Pastoral Care Division Director, and Joseph F. Viti, Program Manager of Clinical Pastoral Education. We also wish to acknowledge the contribution of a number of CPE students who, together with chaplains Roseann Bloom-field and Victor F. Kolch (Pastoral Services Manager), participated in the year-long seminar on interfaith spiritual care held at LHI.[6] Carol Demland, Pastoral Care Division's administrative assistant, graciously provided valuable logistic support.

We are also grateful to several people who helped us during the final phases of the writing and publication process: Joanne Gallardo, Cara Lynn Pfeiffer, Carrie Martens and Heidi Rupley provided secretarial and copy-editing assistance; Mary Epp Klassen designed the cover and the book and prepared it for publication; Christian Snyder and the staff of Pandora Press literally made the book a reality. Last but not least, we wish to acknowledge the financial support for AMBS's interfaith care research given by individual donors that ensured timely publication.

The editors

---

[6] Participants during different stages of the year-long seminar included resident chaplains Lindsay Beeson, Russell Dewell, David Griebel and Sr. Sharlene Kakkattil; and CPE students Steve Evans, Brad Foster, Sheryl Nicholson, Paul Spira, and James Walker.

Introduction

The unfolding process of globalization[1] together with the manifestations of post-modernity[2] are key factors that inform the social context of pastoral care practices in our time. The growing presence of a plurality of faith expressions in our culture, both religious and non-religious,[3] is indeed a major dimension of the social reality. Christian pastoral care specialists, both as practitioners and as pastoral theologians, need to work within, and reflect upon such reality in the light of normative claims of the Christian faith tradition (for instance, convictions about Jesus Christ, the church, the Bible, the Holy Spirit, and the Reign of God). Actually, pastoral

---

[1] The globalization process under way includes political, economic, technological, and cultural dimensions. Interconnected systems of communication, transportation, and political organization tend to weave our world together into a single global locality. Indeed, globalization is restructuring the ways we live in diverse areas such as sexuality, family life, and the socialization of youth. See Anthony Giddens, *Runaway World: How Globalization is Reshaping Our Lives* (New York: Routledge, 2000). For a comprehensive introduction to the subject of globalization, see David Held, Anthony McGrew, David Goldblatt, and Jonathan Perraton, *Global Transformations: Politics, Economics, and Culture* (Cambridge, U.K.: Polity Press, 1999). We agree with authors such as Robert J. Schreiter that "globalization" is the broad category to use in describing the signs of the times, "postmodernity" needing to be viewed within such a larger conceptual framework. See, for instance, Schreiter's *The New Catholicity: Theology Between the Global and the Local* (Maryknoll: Orbis Books, 1997), especially chapter 1.

[2] We are working with a straightforward account of postmodernity: a pluralist society in which not only are many theories and worldviews tolerated and accepted but there is also a profound suspicion of grand theories and theologies, of systems which make claims to truth (which are viewed as inadequate to reality and coercive). As an ideology, *postmodernism* celebrates the pluralism and fragmentation of so-called postmodern societies as a condition in which "true freedom" is possible. Further, postmodernists typically highlight alternative ways of knowing, restate the human value of emotions and feelings, wonder and mystery, and appreciate the experience of a "second naivete" (with an emphasis on the significance of living in the master stories as stories rather than as factual historical accounts). For an overview of the different sources and expressions of postmodernism, and an evaluation from a Christian perspective, see Stanley J. Grenz, *A Primer on Postmodernism* (Grand Rapids: Eerdmans, 1996).

[3] We adopt the understanding of *faith* as a human universal that may or may not find expression in terms of a specific religious tradition and content (beliefs and rituals). It is the understanding articulated by James W. Fowler in his classic work, *Stages of Faith: The Psychology of Human Development and the Quest for Meaning* (San Francisco: Harper & Row, 1981). See also, *Weaving the New Creation: Stages of Faith and the Public Church* (San Francisco: Harper, 1991); *Faithful Change: The Personal and Public Challenges of Postmodern Life* (Nashville: Abingdon Press, 1996); and *Becoming Adult, Becoming Christian*, rev.ed. (San Francisco: Jossey-Bass, 2000).

caregivers have always had to engage in interfaith communication even if they have not always reflected critically and constructively on such phenomenon in a systematic way.[4] Some of them, however, have taken advantage of the contributions of *intercultural* study to pastoral care and counseling, which offers an opportunity for further exploration of *interfaith* pastoral caregiving as a structurally analogous experience.[5]

The main question that the book addresses concerns the effective practice of *therapeutic*[6] *communication* that becomes "good news" of hope and healing in the pastoral care setting of health care institutions. It is our thesis that Christian pastoral caregivers must engage effectively and consistently in the practice of therapeutic communication in interfaith situations as a special way of *caring Christianly*.[7] Further, that they can do so while fully respecting the value, integrity, and resourcefulness of the care receivers'spirituality or faith. Such practice may necessitate the transformation of Christian religious and theological language while remaining focused on the communication of good news for care-receivers regardless of their religious affiliation, the nature of their faith, broadly

---

[4] An exception is the collection of essays in Robert G. Anderson and Mary A. Fukuyama, eds. *Ministry in the Spiritual and Cultural Diversity of Health Care: Increasing the Competency of Chaplains* (New York: The Haworth Pastoral Press, 2004). See also, Sue Wintz and Earl P. Cooper, *Learning Module for Cultural and Spiritual Sensitivity and Quick Guide to Cultures and Spiritual Traditions* (2000), www.professionalchaplains.org. These valuable resources, however, do not include a systematic consideration of theological foundations and perspectives for interfaith spiritual care; further, they do not address the epistemological and methodological issues involved in the interplay between the human sciences and theology, which is essential for an adequate understanding and an effective practice of interfaith caregiving from a Christian perspective.

[5] During the last two decades a number of books addressing the challenges of intercultural caregiving have been published, especially in the areas of counseling and psychotherapy. Recent research connects issues of cross-cultural communication and spirituality, as documented, for example, in Mary A. Fukuyama and Todd D. Sevig, Integrating Spirituality into Multicultural Counseling (Thousand Oaks, Ca.: Sage, 1999). On the one hand, interfaith spiritual caregiving can be viewed and practiced as a special form of intercultural caregiving, as caregivers and care receivers share meaning and values. On the other hand, the former presents unique features pertaining not only to the specific content of the verbal and non-verbal interactions between caregiver and care receiver but, especially, to the norms that guide and help to evaluate the very quality and effectiveness of those interactions.

[6] "Therapeutic" is here used with the twofold denotation of *ministerial* (from *therapeutes*, one who attends or serves, ministers) as well as *clinical* (literally, at the bed side). Simply put, then, *therapeutic communication* denotes the kind of verbal and nonverbal interaction experienced by the care-receiver as deeply caring in the senses of nurturing, supporting, guiding, reconciling and healing.

[7] By "caring Christianly" we mean the kind of spiritual caregiving that stems from a biblically grounded and theologically sound vision of reality and the good life in the light of God; a disposition to care unconditionally in the manner of Jesus as a form of love of neighbor; and a sense of vocation experienced as partnership with the Spirit. These dimensions of their Christian faith define the caregivers' identity, normative framework, and ministry work. This project assumes that there is an ongoing systematic reflection on the notion of caring Christianly.

speaking (including, for instance, religious and non-religious humanism) and the overall quality of their spirituality.[8]

Purpose of the research and publication

The research and writing project leading to this publication was designed to meet the following goals: to explore the dynamics of interfaith spiritual care as an exercise of practical and pastoral theology; to identify reliable guidelines for competent practice of interfaith spiritual care duly contextualized; and to invite further cooperation on this subject among practitioners and scholars.

The project addressed the question of what is desirable and appropriate (that is, clinically effective as well as theologically sound) therapeutic communication in interfaith pastoral care encounters. Such overarching purpose determined the fourfold focus of the study that characterizes the structure and overall approach of practical theology as a discipline,[9] as indicated below in terms of key sets of issues explored in the book.

First, we characterized spiritual caregiving situations with care receivers who represent a variety of faith traditions, including non-religious faith traditions. Second, we considered philosophical and human science foundations of interfaith care. Third, we articulated biblical, theological, and ethical norms that support and guide interfaith communication in pastoral caregiving. Finally, we identified factors such as personal dispositions (values and virtues, attitudes), competencies, practices and approaches conducive to effective therapeutic communication in interfaith caregiving situations.

The aim of this project is to enhance the practice of Christian spiritual caregivers in the hospital as they encounter the growing plurality of faith traditions and expressions among care receivers and colleagues. The book is therefore intended for chaplains, pastors and other caregivers, such as counselors and psychotherapists, both in training—especially CPE students and residents—and already in practice.

---

[8] The term "spirituality" is meant here as the overarching construct, connoting a fundamental human potential as well as need for meaning and value and the disposition for relationship with a transcendent power. "Faith" is used by us as denoting patterned ways of being "spiritual" in terms of Fowler's contribution.

[9] For a clear and systematic discussion of the four tasks of practical theology as a discipline—decriptive-empirical, interpretive, normative, and pragmatic—see Richard R. Osmer, *Practical Theology: An Introduction* (Grand Rapids: Eerdmans, 2008).

Content of the book

The two chapters in Part I—"Identity and vocation of the spiritual caregiver"—present first person accounts and reflective observations of the dynamics of interfaith communication in pastoral caregiving. They address questions such as what actually goes on in interfaith care, what are the key issues we can identify in a given interfaith encounter, especially focusing on the caregiver as a ministering person. They also include interpretive analyses of the interfaith care dynamics and the overarching orientation of interfaith care.

The two chapters in the second part of the book—"Bases for a theological framework for interfaith care"—deal with biblical and theological norms. This focus on the normative dimension and task of our practical theological strategy illumines the key question of what criteria we identify for *excellence* and *faithfulness* in interfaith spiritual care from a Christian perspective. It further suggests that we should consider additional or alternative ethical and theological norms representing other theological traditions.

Five chapters in the third part—"Other windows to competent ministry practice"—illustrate the following issues: how spiritual caregivers can approach an interfaith situation and remain engaged as reflective practitioners; the benefits of consultation and group case discussion; and commonalities and differences in interfaith care provided in public and faith based hospitals.

Finally, Part IV—"Attending to the socio-cultural context"—consists of two chapters with extended references to social and spiritual location. The first one, focusing on a Canadian context, proposes that the primary focus of attention of the caregiver must be the faith or spiritual process of the care receiver (rather than the content of specific beliefs as such). The second, addressing Hawaiian reality, offers a comprehensive discussion of reflective practice, including a detailed analysis of assessment and intervention issues.

The epilogue summarizes essential features of excellence in the manner of an emerging profile of wise interfaith spiritual care. In the last section of the book, the selected bibliography represents an invitation to further thought, discussion, and collaboration.

Part 1

Identity and vocation of the spiritual caregiver

A journey of soul companioning
Personal, vocational, and ministry reflections

Joseph F. Viti

Christian caregivers in a hospital setting soon discover that there is a growing need to minister to others regardless of their religious affiliation, lack of religious affiliation, the nature of their faith, and their type of spirituality. Interfaith ministry is at the forefront of the practice of pastoral care. In this essay I document the value of integrating soul companioning as a key component of interfaith ministry. I have come to understand the effectiveness of soul companioning from my own personal, vocational, and ministerial journey. Personal, vocational, ministerial, and soul companioning are the main headings of this chapter. I begin by sharing about the roots of my personal interfaith journey which I trace back to my childhood experiences when I was exposed to a diversity of culture and faith. These experiences were foundational. During my theological formation at the Catholic Theological Union my approach to theological truth became ecumenical. As I responded to my calling as a chaplain, I initially understood the value of forming a pastoral relationship as the basis for an inclusive ministry to a diversity of faiths. But it is precisely the faith beliefs of the chaplain rooted in theological conviction that set the tension off in ways that hinder ministry as illustrated by the verbatim I present between a Christian chaplain and a Jewish patient. The tension evolves from differences between religious beliefs and relationships into the tension of ministering to a stranger. The ensuing dynamic becomes less theologically focused and more relationally centered. Biblical references such as Genesis 18:1–15, Luke 24:13–35, and Matthew 35:31–46 underline the value of hospitality as a way to relate to strangers by understanding their spiritual needs and potential. The focus of hospitality

Joseph F. Viti, M.Div., is a supervisor and Program Manager of Clinical Pastoral Education, Pastoral Care Division, at Lutheran Hospital of Indiana, Fort Wayne, Indiana.

is coming to know the stranger as a person with spiritual needs as well as resources. The person, not doctrine or dogma, becomes the focal point of attention. Finally, this leads to the pastoral relationship of soul companioning. As a soul companion the chaplain encourages patients to take responsibility for their beliefs by giving them the freedom to get in touch with the spiritual needs of their soul.

Personal journey

I was raised in a small town in eastern Pennsylvania called Nazareth. It was in this town that I learned to appreciate diversity from a social and religious point of view. I have memories of a peaceful, clean, charming town of friendly people. I was born in 1945, so I am referring to the decades of the fifties and sixties. Comparatively speaking, it was a more simple lifestyle back in those days. The environment was very safe. Sometimes homeowners forgot to lock their doors at night, and felt perfectly safe. The impact of the immigrants from Europe was still experienced by the way the economy of Nazareth was carved up. Most of the bars and barber-shops in town were owned and operated by the Italians, most of the retail was in the hands of the Jewish people, and the surrounding farms in the outlying districts were owned by the famous Pennsylvania Dutch. My dad was a barber, and I can still remember some of his Pennsylvania Dutch customers trying to teach me a few words in Dutch when I would hang around my dad's barber-shop as a boy. They succeeded in teaching me how to say dog, cat, and potato in Pennsylvania Dutch (hund, katz, and grumberr). My folks, who originated from Italy, really got a "kick" out of that. There was a rich diversity among the entrepreneurs of Nazareth. Nazareth was surrounded by many limestone-rich quarries from which the cement industry thrived. The Nazareth Cement Company employed thousands of workers. The cement industry had an impact on the trade of the store owners. The store owners had to deal with the ups and downs of the cement industry as well as the income of the farmers. So the store owners had a lot to talk about among themselves because they were bonded together by the economy of a small town. Their conversation produced a thriving relationship. When my dad, mother, brother, and I returned home from our three-week vacation in Italy during the summer of 1965, all of the store owners gathered in my dad's barber-shop on the Monday morning he reopened his shop. They all welcomed him back, and they wanted to hear all about his experience revisiting the land of his boyhood. That gathering in my dad's barber-shop symbolized a caring social community. They felt a sense of bonding. What comes to mind about the former shop owners of Nazareth is the common ground they discovered in their struggles as entrepreneurs. Despite their cultural and religious differences they discovered a common language that fostered values of respect and mutuality. When they spoke to one another they listened with sensitivity, understanding, and validated experiences. The inherent differences did not prevent them from affirming one another's humanity and supporting each other in the struggles they faced as entrepreneurs.

We lived around the corner from the Moravian church. The Moravians, a Protestant group, founded the town back in 1740. They predated the Revolutionary War. One Sunday morning I innocently walked into the Moravian church before their worship service. The janitor recognized me. He walked over to where I was sitting, took me by the hand, and walked me down the stairs to the Sunday school. The janitor and the Sunday school teachers all knew who I was. They were aware that I was the barber's son whose family was Italian and Roman Catholic. They saw no harm in letting me stay and participate with the other children in their weekly Sunday school. I had a wonderful time and took a great interest in Sunday school. I returned several times on my own. When my parents found out about what I was up to on Sunday mornings, they were shocked beyond words. When I expressed my great delight with Sunday school, my sister, Nancy, and brother, Victor, begged our parents to accompany me the next Sunday. My parents consented, which was a surprise. Eventually the Moravian pastor, who was one of my dad's customers, invited the entire family to join the Moravian church. Our family quickly became the subject of a lot of talk around town. "Can you imagine this Italian Roman Catholic family considering joining the Moravian church?" When the Roman Catholic priest heard about what was going on, he approached my dad for a stern conversation. He said you need to make a decision. You are either Roman Catholic or Moravian, not both. He forced us to make a definitive decision. I have a vague memory of my family sitting around the kitchen table talking about what we were going to do. My dad wanted to join the Moravian church because he anticipated lots of new customers to his barber shop. My sister, brother, and I wanted to join the Moravian church. We liked Sunday school. My mother is the one who made the decision. She said, "I was born a Catholic, and I will die a Catholic." And that was it! The decision was made.

As I look back on my experience with the Moravian church, I had many pleasant memories of learning about God in ways that were fun and educational. One of the first seeds of faith was planted in me by a

Protestant church. It was, for me, a rich, lively, exciting experience. I was not aware of it at the time, but it was a soulful experience. God became present to me in a way that was relevant and diverse even though I innocently crossed over some boundaries. I was also fortunate I had parents who were willing to go with the spirit and not the rules. Their openness put our family in a position to consider options about where we were going to worship and how we were going to express our faith. I learned that there is more than one way to practice one's faith without impunity and judgment. At a very early age it was clear to me that there is not one way to God but several!

All of this freedom I was experiencing as a young boy came to a crashing head when I entered Catholic school at the fourth grade level. From kindergarten through third grade I attended public school. When I was about ten years old the Catholic church in Nazareth, Holy Family Church, completed construction on a brand new school, grades one to eight. My mother and dad decided to transfer us children from public school to Holy Family Parochial School. My Roman Catholic education began with the fourth grade. At some point during religion class I recall being taught that the church of Jesus Christ subsists in the Catholic church, because the Roman Catholic church had the unbroken line of apostolic succession and the fullness of the Eucharist. During the days prior to The Second Vatican Council, we were taught that there was no salvation outside the Catholic church. I understood that as much as any child could, but I really had trouble with that when the religious sisters who taught us counseled us not to play with Protestant children. The religious sisters were aware that most of the children at Holy Family School lived in neighborhoods populated by families who belonged to the Catholic church. They may have overlooked students like my brother, sister, and I who lived in a primarily Protestant neighborhood. I recall that when my sister, Nancy, and my brother, Victor, attended public school, a Jewish girl who lived down the street from us would, now and then, stop by our house on the way to school, and we would all walk to school together. Looking back on that experience, I am certain that the religious sisters had our best interests at heart. It does, however, bring up an interesting issue. I wonder how people of other Christian faiths felt when they heard that the Catholic church taught no salvation outside the Catholic church. Some felt indifferent. Some felt challenged. Others may have felt hurt and offended. There are times when churches adhere to a particular doctrine that brings up relational issues. The doctrine of no salvation outside the Church caused conflict between me and my playmates in our neighborhood. I wonder what they would have thought if I had told them about no salvation outside the Catholic church. How would that have influenced our relationship as playmates? Doctrine was potentially cancelling out relational values I had developed, and the relational values were threatening to the doctrine. There was a tension between the doctrine I learned at the Catholic school and the relationships I had spontaneously developed as a child. My brother, sister, and I quietly ignored what the religious sisters said and continued to enjoy our Protestant/Jewish playmates. I felt encouraged when the Vatican II document, "Dogmatic Constitution on the Church (Lumen Gentium)," emphatically stated that there is salvation outside the Roman Catholic church.[1]

My childhood experience sharply focuses the pastoral care dilemma. Pastoral care is relationally driven. There are times when the pastoral relationship is threatened because of doctrinal differences not only within Christian churches, but even more so in non-Christian churches such as Jewish, Islamic, Buddhist, and Hindu. I certainly accept the teachings of the Roman Catholic church and want to be faithful to its magisterium. In this country people live in a diverse society including different cultures and different belief systems. With the influx of Hispanics, Asians, Hindus, Buddhists, and Muslims we continue to be a "melting pot" after a fashion. Proclaiming that there is only one way to God tends to create too many distinctions between right and wrong, inclusive and exclusive, the saved verses the damned. There are many expressions of Christianity and, perhaps, the multiplicity is pointing to the many faith needs that are met in different ways. If we listened to one another with sensitivity and openness we could deepen the truth about what we believe. Division does not create an understanding. Reaching out to one another does.

While studying for my M.Div. degree at the Catholic Theological Union in Chicago, Illinois, I had a discussion with a religious woman about ecumenism. During our discussion she said that no one Christian church had the fullness of the truth about who God is, what we are to believe about God, and how we are to go about our eternal salvation. She compared the Christian church to a diamond. Not any one church has the fullness of the truth, but each church is like a facet of the diamond. If you turn the diamond in a particular direction to let the light shine through the diamond, you may get the Lutheran expression. If you turn the diamond another way, you may get the Methodist expression. If you

---

[1] Walter M. Abbot and Joseph Gallagher, *The Documents of Vatican II* (New York: Guild Press, 1966), 33–35.

turn the diamond again, you may get the Roman Catholic expression, and so on. Together, as one diamond, we all have the truth. That made sense to me. It was then that I realized that the truth was found not by reinforcement of the doctrine/dogma of any one religious denomination, but by studying the differences and/or gaps between them.

Vocational journey

As a student of Clinical Pastoral Education (CPE) at Allentown State Hospital, a state-run institution for the mentally ill, I soon realized that mental illness does not discriminate among Protestants, Catholics, Jews, or Muslims. I was dealing with our weak human nature. Many of the patients I ministered to reached out to God, at times, in delusional ways; and at other times, in ways that were sane. My ministry did not consist in trying to figure out who believed what, but the key to my ministry was to establish a rapport of trust. There was a strong relational component driving my ministry. I believed God worked through my ministry in an incarnational way. God became present through the confusion and delusion of the person of the patient and through me. Looking to the patient to establish the agenda was a way to relate to the spiritual needs of the patient that did not necessarily involve doctrine and/or differing beliefs. A ministry of healing driven by relationship was the priority.

However, I have discovered as a supervisor for the Association of Clinical Pastoral Education (ACPE) that there are times when the relational quality of pastoral care relationships is not sufficient to bridge the gap. Below is a verbatim that illustrates the problem. This verbatim was presented in a scheduled case study conference by a CPE student during a unit of CPE. Feedback was given to him by me and the peer group.

The patient is an 87-year-old woman known as Mrs. Wheatley. At the time the verbatim was written she was a resident of a nursing home recovering from a broken ankle. She is Jewish. The chaplain, a Christian, is making a random visit. This was the third time the chaplain visited Mrs. Wheatley. He describes her as a vibrant person of 87 who is now showing signs of depression because she is adjusting to many life changes. Her fractured ankle was caused by a spell of dizziness which led to a fall. The physical cause of the dizziness is not known at the time of the visit. After rehabilitation at the nursing home, the plans are that she will live with her son who has recently moved into a new home. The chaplain has discovered that Mrs. Wheatley recently lost her brother-in-law who died in Los Angeles, California. She grieved his death. She wanted to travel and attend the funeral, but could not due to the fractured ankle. The chaplain did not know about the death of her brother-in-law. He discovered it during the visit. The chaplain's goal was to comfort her with his presence. Mrs. Wheatley had been in this room for approximately two weeks, so she does not have many of her personal belongings in the room. As the chaplain entered the room, he could tell from the patient's appearance that she was grieving. She was well dressed, well groomed, and wearing some makeup.

Dialogue

P = Patient

C = Chaplain

C1   Good morning, Mrs. Wheatley. How are you?

P1   Not very well, my brother-in-law just died yesterday.

C2   I am sorry to hear that. Were you close?

P2   Yes, but he was in L.A. And now I won't be able to go to the funeral like I would have if I weren't here.

C3   Is your sister still living?

P3   Yes

C4   How is she doing?

P4   She'll get through it; she has to be strong. I was, when my husband passed away.

C5   When did he die?

P5   In 1989.

C6   Do you miss him?

P6   Oh my yes, but we had a good life.

C7   Does your brother-in-law's death conjure up memories and feelings from when your husband died?

P7   Some.

C8   What else are you feeling now?

P8   Bad because I can't be there for my sister.

C9   Is there a sense of guilt at not being able to be there?

P9   Yes.

C10 Does your sister know where you are, and what has happened to you?

P10 Yes.

C11 Do you think she is upset with you for not being able to come out?

P11 No, I do feel bad. I know that she isn't angry with me, but I was
     close to her husband and I feel bad about not being able to be there
     for the funeral to say good-bye.

(At this point her roommate was brought back into the room with her
     two daughters. The conversation came to an end.)

C12 Can I stop back, and see how you are doing in a few days?

P12 I would like that, thank you.

Assessment of the pastoral visit

The chaplain was deeply motivated to help Mrs. Wheatley, but he experienced a theological distance because he is Christian and she is Jewish.
The chaplain could have brought up that issue, but did not. It is ignoring the "elephant" in the room. This may explain why the visit is brief,
and why he did not follow the patient's agenda. It also explains why the
chaplain did not offer a prayer. The chaplain claims that despite the
theological distance, he enjoyed visiting with Mrs. Wheatley. Generally
the chaplain did not focus on the relationship between Mrs. Wheatley
and her brother-in-law. Instead he inquires about grief over the loss of
Mrs. Wheatley's husband who died in 1989. He also raises the issue of the
relationship with her sister. This was a valid concern, but the chaplain's
timing is bad, because he uses the relationship with her sister to distract
from dealing with the funeral. Below is a detailed critique of the verbatim
based on the feedback the chaplain received.

Because of what Mrs. Wheatley says in P2, the chaplain, in C3, had
an opportunity to ask Mrs. Wheatley what going to the funeral means to
her. Instead, he changes the subject and focuses on Mrs. Wheatley's sister.
Instead of asking, "Is your sister still living?" he could have asked a more
timely question such as, "How would the funeral be a source of consolation
to you?" It may have been helpful for her grief to draw that out. There may
have been some specific parts of the funeral that she would have found
meaningful. In C4, the chaplain continues to focus on Mrs. Wheatley's
sister. In P4, the chaplain learns new information concerning the death
of the patient's husband. In C7, the chaplain pursues the possibility that
Mrs. Wheatley continues to have some feelings of grief over the death of
her husband who died in 1989. In P7, Mrs Wheatley indicates that she
continues to experience feelings of grief over her husband's death, but
her feelings are not that intense that she wants to continue to reflect on
them. At this point it is safe to say that the chaplain is not following the
patient's agenda as he could, but is pursuing his own agenda. Finally in

C8, the chaplain invites Mrs. Wheatley to focus on her feelings, "What else are you feeling now?" In P8, Mrs. Wheatley shares feelings about her sister, and this leads to feelings of guilt Mrs. Wheatley has about not being there for her sister. In P11, Mrs. Wheatley brings up the topic again, on her own initiative, about her sadness over not being there for the funeral. This is the second time Mrs. Wheatley has brought up this topic because this is a soul-felt desire. Her feelings of grief about her brother-in-law and how she relates them to her faith in Yahweh come together here. There is significant meaning for her here.

In her book, *Listening for the Soul*, Jean Stairs says it well: "The goal of soul companionship is to help people listen for the soul and for the presence of God in their daily work and lives."[2] The chaplain focused on his agenda because he felt threatened by religious differences. We see here the strength of Mrs. Wheatley's soul struggling for solace despite the chaplain's hesitation to honor her agenda. The chaplain missed an opportunity to become her soul companion. He could have responded to her without threat to his beliefs merely by being personally present to her. Soul companioning could have been significant here because the concern could have been placed on the spiritual needs of Mrs. Wheatley, not on doctrinal or dogmatic differences. He could have found common space and holy ground with her despite religious differences. I will discuss more on soul companioning later on in the article.

If Mrs. Wheatley cannot go to the funeral, then how will she say good-bye to her brother-in-law whom she is close to? The chaplain may have wanted to do this, but the visit was interrupted by the roommate coming back into the room. Because the chaplain perceives a *theological* distance, there is also a *relational* distance. During the critical evaluation among the CPE students, the chaplain, who made the visit, openly expressed feelings of conflict over ministering to Mrs. Wheatley. He wanted to reach out to her, but felt hindered by theological differences. It is interesting to note that he does not ask Mrs. Wheatley if she would like him to contact her rabbi. The chaplain does feel a sense of relating to Mrs. Wheatley's grief. He does not know how to go about bridging the gap, however.

By bringing up the theological differences, the chaplain could have shared his unfamiliarity with the Jewish funeral. This would have created an opportunity for Mrs. Wheatley to bridge the gap. It is not the obligation of patients to educate chaplains. We have a mandate to educate ourselves about religious differences. But by expressing theological differences,

---

[2] Jean Stairs, *Listening for the Soul* (Minneapolis: Fortress Press, 2000), 142.

the chaplain is bringing the limits of his ministry out in the open where something can be done to recognize and validate the difference as being OK. Because the chaplain does not verbalize the difference, it becomes a shadow of the ministerial event. Shadows have a way of blocking the light which can illuminate the limits of pastoral relationships as a spark of knowledge and information that can begin to take away those limits. It could place the chaplain in a position of openly claiming how he is prepared to minister, and how he is not prepared. This openness could be the foundation of bridging the chaplain-patient relationship. Sharing of limits would open up the dialogue for the benefit of the patient and the learning of the chaplain.

Prayer is one way the chaplain has of elevating the death of Mrs. Wheatley's brother-in-law to a higher power. It is one of the ways chaplains communicate that they represent the wisdom and authority of faith. The chaplain may not have prayed with Mrs. Wheatley because he felt he may have to compromise his faith in the Trinity, particularly Jesus Christ. This is one of the limits of interfaith ministry that many chaplains fear. The thinking goes something like this, "If I minister to a non-Christian, what beliefs am I going to have to give up? Will I discover myself ministering in a way that compromises my faith? What will I have to accept that I will regret?" In this particular ministerial event the chaplain could have read a psalm from the Hebrew Scriptures which are also part of the Christian Scriptures. He could have asked Mrs. Wheatley to offer a prayer. He could have asked Mrs. Wheatley if she would object to invoking the Universal God. Biblically, one could argue that Jesus Christ is Jewish. I do not believe that God is Roman Catholic or Lutheran or Methodist or Episcopalian or Muslim or Buddhist or Hindu. God is God. We will never truly understand who God is. God is beyond our understanding and our knowledge. When chaplains minister to patients, a window of opportunity opens up for God to "enter the room," so to speak. Whether or not God enters the room with divine presence, grace, or healing, is up to God. We have no control over God. We can invoke the Divine with prayer. The chaplain could have prayed to the God who is in the room, or the God who is present to the ministerial event.

Ministry journey

I believe that God is present to ministers of pastoral care through their calling. In his article, "Spiritual Windsurfing," John Janka says that the call of ministry "is to believe in the revealed truth so deeply that we are fundamentally changed by it and compelled to invite others to live as though this truth is the only reality of consequence in their lives."[3] This understanding of call takes into account that ministers not only believe in their call, but are also willing to commit their life to it. The commitment implies that the meaning of their life revolves around this call. It is what puts "wind" in their vocational sails. It is a reason to get up in the morning, and a prayer of hope that is said before sleep. It can become a passion for life that one struggles with, fails at, succeeds at, and that even makes our souls bleed. We feel so strongly and deeply about our calling that we want to invite others to become impacted by it, and take up that same divine "spark" for their lives. We hope others will be as moved by it as we are so that it impacts the way they live their lives. We hope they develop values and priorities that influence their lifestyle. Ultimately we hope our ministry leads the people we serve to have a deeper relationship with God, and helps them on their spiritual journey.

Sometimes, it is this very deep commitment that can become an obstruction to interfaith ministry. The chaplain who ministered to Mrs. Wheatley felt that he was a stranger to her Jewish faith and was faced with compromising his commitment. When chaplains tend to back away from interfaith ministry, they see that as self-care, that is caring for their faith and giving testimony to their integrity and authenticity. Care for one's faith and pastoral care begin to compete. There is a tension that develops. Ministering to a person of a different faith for the first time, can be a threatening experience for some chaplains. I recall when I took my first unit of CPE at Virginia Baptist Hospital in Lynchburg, Virginia, I experienced a threat to my Roman Catholic morality when I made a pre-surgery visit one particular evening. I knocked on the door of a private room. The door was ajar. I was invited to enter by a couple who was in the room. The woman was sitting in bed sipping a glass of champagne, and her husband was sitting in a chair next to the bed also enjoying a glass of champaign. I was delightfully surprised, and asked them what was going on. They explained to me that the wife was having her fallopian tubes tied the next day. They were no longer going to have children. As a married couple, they were celebrating the end of one era in their lives, and now they were moving on to the next phase of their marriage and family life. They wanted to honor and celebrate the event with a glass of champaign. As a Roman Catholic, I strongly disagreed with that form of birth control; and so I said some words of congratulations, and removed myself from the room as quicky and graciously as I could. I did not even offer to say a

---

[3] John Janka, "Spiritual Windsurfing: Exploring the Context for Evaluation" in *Congregational Resources* (Bethesda, MD: Alban Institute, 2004), 2.

prayer for the wife that the surgery would go well. My quick departure was an indication that in my own mind I judged the surgery to be wrong. As I look back on that ministerial event, I shudder at my lack of sensitivity and regard for the couple. If I would do anything differently, I would tell them that I am Roman Catholic, and although I cannot celebrate with them in fact, I want to celebrate with them in spirit. In certain instances of morality the lines of difference are not always black and white. There are gray areas. This instance was one of them. Just because someone else disagrees with me, how is that a threat to my morality? There is a value to being a non-anxious presence at those times to honor and respect others, to honor and respect each other in our differences. In a parallel way, when I minister to someone who is not Christian, it is a matter of being sensitive to differences and caring for differences. That approach is more pastoral than being judgmental, aloof, distant, and feeling threatened. People who believe differently than we do are considered strange to us because we are not familiar with what they believe. We do not feel we are on common ground with them, and that makes us feel uncomfortable. We become hesitant to relate to them. As ministers of pastoral care we need to develop a ministry to the stranger.

Ministering to the stranger

Whenever I minister to a person who is not Christian, who is Jewish, Muslim, Buddhist, or Hindu, I am ministering to a stranger from a pastoral point of view. The stranger symbolizes faith. As Parker Palmer says, "Faith is a venture into the unknown, into the realms of mystery, away from the safe and comfortable and secure."[4] Faith is stepping into mystery. Mystery is who God is. Becoming acquainted with God is departing from those areas of our lives that are comfortable and secure. Relating to God is a "stretch." Sometimes, when we believe in God, we make ourselves vulnerable to the challenges God has for us. When chaplains step into a hospital room to visit a patient, they are entering the realm of Mystery. Patients in a hospital are often in physical, emotional, and spiritual crisis. They look to the chaplain to guide them through confusing feelings they may have about their relationship to God. Chaplains can do little to prepare for the visit. They need to become spontaneous and go with the "flow" of what the patient wants to deal with. The authority in the room becomes the patient and his or her spiritual agenda. As we read in

---

[4] Parker J. Palmer, *The Company of Strangers* (New York: The Crossroad Publishing Co., 1997), 56.

the book of Hebrews, "Keep on loving one another as Christian brothers and sisters. Remember to welcome strangers in your homes. There were some who did that and welcomed angels without knowing it." Hebrews 13:1–2. The stranger is a key figure in certain biblical stories of faith: Genesis 18:1–15, Luke 24:13–35, Matthew 25:31–46.

In Genesis 18:1–15, strangers appear to Sarah and Abraham to announce that Sarah, who is beyond the childbearing years, will give birth to Isaac, the second patriarch of the Jewish people. As the story unfolds, it becomes evident that the strangers are angels who have come to announce God's promise to Abraham and Sarah. They struggle with the message the strangers deliver. The only way they can validate their message is with their faith. But Abraham did welcome the strangers by showing hospitality. When he saw the three strangers, he ran to meet them, bowing down to them until his face touched the ground (verse 2). In verse 3, he invites them into his home to serve them. He brings them water so they can wash their feet, and invites them to rest under the shade of the sacred trees at Mamre (verse 4). He tells them that they have honored him by coming to his home, and asks Sarah to bake bread for them. He then picks out a tender, fattened calf from the herd, and asks a servant to prepare it for the strangers. He serves this food to the strangers with milk and cream (verses 5–8). By being attentive to the needs of strangers they become less strange and more familiar. Hospitality recognizes that the stranger has needs. Knowing the needs of another is the beginning of knowledge that makes the stranger less of an unknown person and more of a known person whom we can help. Creating an atmosphere of comfort gives strangers the message that they are welcomed. Despite the fact that I do not know you; I want to treat you with honor and respect. I want to be concerned for your well-being. I want to put you at ease. This hospitality creates the atmosphere for dialogue and establishes the possibility of the non-judgmental listening Carl Rogers speaks about for arriving at understanding.[5] After the strangers ate, they asked Abraham where Sarah was. Abraham replied that she was in the tent. One of the strangers then announced to the couple that nine months from now Sarah will have a child. After Abraham offered hospitality, the strangers communicated their message. If Abraham and Sarah had not offered hospitality to strangers, they could have missed the message of fulfillment.

When chaplains minister to patients of a different faith, they are strangers to one another. A learning curve for chaplains is how to effec-

---

[5] Carl R. Rogers, *Client Centered Therapy* (Boston: Houghton Mifflin Company, 1965), 45.

tively participate in the ministry of strangers. As Henri Nouwen points out in his book *Reaching Out*, we need to take the initiative to establish hospitality. If we do not, the potential remains there for the chaplain to become infected with fear and hostility, threatening the chaplain's faith and blocking dialogue and understanding.[6] It does not mean that we become so attentive to their needs that strangers become "putty" in our hands. It means that we allow them free space where strangers can be themselves without having to change.[7] From a pastoral point of view, Christian chaplains offer strangers—Jews, Muslims, Hindus, Buddhists, and others—hospitality which does not charm them into accepting our God, but opens up an opportunity that gives them the freedom to accept and find their God in a deeper way and discover a new message that addresses their spiritual needs.

In Luke 24:13–35, the risen Jesus and the two disciples on the road to Emmaus discover themselves as strangers. Not only do they not recognize one another, but the two disciples are deeply distressed about the outcome of the life of Jesus. In verse 21 they express their distress by saying, "And we had hoped that he would be the one who was going to set Israel free!" After the two disciples continue to express their regret, sorrow, disillusionment, and confusion, Jesus explains the scriptures to them, beginning with the books of Moses and the writings of all the prophets (verse 27). As they came near the village, Jesus acted as if he were going to travel on, but the two disciples asked Jesus to stay with them. They recognized Jesus in the breaking of the bread. Jesus disappeared from their sight. "Wasn't it like a fire burning in us when he talked to us on the road and explained the Scriptures to us?" (verse 32). Their regret, sorrow, disillusionment, and confusion turned to enlightenment and enthusiasm as they ran all the way back to Jerusalem to tell the eleven apostles that they recognized Jesus in the breaking of the bread (verse 35). The two disciples, perhaps out of their desperation, offered hospitality to someone who looked like a stranger. They invited him into their home and sat down to eat with Jesus. It is in the breaking of the bread that they recognized Jesus as the risen Lord. Jesus offered hospitality to the two disciples by being attentive to their feelings of regret, sorrow, disillusionment, and confusion. He took the time and patience to explain the Scriptures to them. In a sense he informed their faith and invited them to believe from a different point of view. The two disciples freely affirmed their new-found faith in

---

[6] Henri J. Nouwen, *Reaching Out* (New York: Image Book Doubleday, 1986), 69.
[7] Ibid., 71.

the breaking of the bread. The hospitality became mutual and the two disciples arrived at a new experience of recognizing who Jesus really is. The stranger of Jesus brought the two disciples beyond their limits to a new faith and a new vision. The vision inspired them and reignited their faith, motivating them to tell others. Strangers may look like shadows, but they have the potential to enlighten truth, reignite passion, and deliver a vision for life. Jesus touched the souls of the two disciples as he taught them, "Wasn't it like a fire burning in us when he talked to us on the road and explained the Scriptures to us?" (verse 32). Jesus was a soul companion for them.

In Matthew 25:31–46, Jesus emphasizes the value of "welcoming the stranger" (verse 38). In this passage the stranger is used to represent all those who suffer and are considered among the lowliest.[8] It is their strangeness which makes us hesitant to minister to them. We feel anxious and threatened by them. What is significant here is that Jesus identifies with the stranger. "I tell you, whenever you refused to help one of these least important ones, you refused to help me" (verse 40). As spiritual caregivers we need to take our soul companioning very seriously.

Soul companioning

Jean Stairs defines soul as "the spiritual essence of one's existence expressed through body, mind, or any other facet of our being."[9] In Genesis 2:7, soul could be understood as the breath of life God gave to Adam. Soul, in the Hebrew language means, "neck."[10] The neck contains the jugular vein, nerves that are connected to the brain and spine that connects the rest of the body to the head. Soul then gives us a vital connection to God as the life force, a sense of wholeness, but also a sense of interior presence about ourselves. When someone touches our soul, they reach the center of who we are. In John 4:1–42, we have the story from the Christian Scriptures about Jesus touching the soul of a Samaritan woman, one who, according to the custom at that time, was not permitted to speak with Jesus, a man and a Jew. When Jesus asks the woman for a drink of water she replies, "You are a Jew and I am a Samaritan, so how can you ask me for a drink?" (verse 9). This limited them in their conversation with each other. The Samaritan woman was also limited by her lifestyle of broken relationships which may have caused her to be defensive due to

---

[8] Palmer, *The Company of Strangers*, 64.

[9] Stairs, *Listening for the Soul*, 10.

[10] For a reference to the Hebrew meaning of "soul," see Eugene H. Peterson, *Christ Plays In Ten Thousand Places* (Grand Rapids, MI. Eerdmans, 2005), 36.

her self-esteem issue.[11] So the relationship between Jesus and the woman does not get off to a good start. Jesus listens to her objections, such as, "I am a Samaritan, so how can you ask me for a drink?" (verse 9). "You don't have a bucket, and the well is deep. Where would you get that life-giving water? It was our ancestor Jacob who gave us this well; he and his sons and his flocks all drank from it. You don't claim to be better than Jacob, do you?" (verses 11–12). Despite all of her objections, Jesus holds her attention with his promise of living water. In verse 14, Jesus promises to give the Samaritan water that is life-giving and will have eternal life. In verse 15, the woman expresses a great desire for this living water. She says, "Then I will never be thirsty again, nor will I have to come here to draw water" (verse 15). Up until this point in their conversation, Jesus is emphasizing the spiritual, and the Samaritan woman is more concerned with the practical and mundane. Jesus then asks her to call her husband in verse 16. Jesus helps her to understand her need for the spiritual freedom he is giving witness to. Jesus heard the nonverbal misery and unhappiness in her objections. Jesus reflects to her what he has heard from the conversation. He pinpoints that relational area in her life that is causing her emotional pain. He surprises her with his knowledge of her sexual life which is personal, private, and potentially shameful.[12] Jesus implies that he has a sense about her false patterns of connectedness.[13] He does not relate to her in an accusatory way of blaming, punishing or judging, but relates to her in a way that gives her the opportunity to know herself from a new perspective. She becomes free to fully know herself, see herself, and be herself.[14] With this new self-knowledge she, without shame, goes to her neighbors to say, "Come and see the man who told me everything I have ever done" (verse 30). Through the conversation Jesus helps the woman come to know herself more deeply and get in touch with her longing for relationships that are freeing, not binding. In a sense Jesus hears her into speech, "Come and see the man …" Her proclamation reflects her new-found freedom from shame. Jesus addresses the personal areas of her life that hinder her from spiritual freedom.

Soul companioning is significant for chaplains ministering to people

---

[11] See the reference to the Samaritan woman at the well in Jeanne Stevenson-Moessner, *Through the Eyes of Women* (Minneapolis: Fortress Press, 1996), 329.

[12] For a reference to how Jesus helps the Samaritan woman to see herself, see Margaret Guenther, *Holy Listening* (Boston: Cowley Publications, 1992), 50.

[13] Stevenson-Moessner, *Through the Eyes of Women*, 28.

[14] Guenther, *Holy Listening*, 50.

of different faiths because the concern is placed on the spiritual needs of the person rather than on the religious differences. Soul companioning helps chaplains listen for the spiritual misery patients may be experiencing, and how they can help without changing or compromising their own faith convictions. Just as Jesus heard the Samaritan woman into speech, chaplains do the same with people of other faiths (Isaiah 50:4). Chaplains listen carefully to the person they are ministering to, but are also open to the promptings of the Spirit. This requires chaplains to educate themselves about the various beliefs and religious practices of Jews, Muslims, Buddhists, Hindus, and other people. It also requires chaplains to have a non-anxious presence. On the one hand if I anticipate that my belief is going to be threatened, I may become anxious. On the other hand why should what another believes cause me to become afraid? I do not want to have a weak and dependent faith. I need an autonomous faith that can stand on its own. Chaplains who minister to others of different faiths need a conversant faith. A conversant faith is one that can dialogue and sort out differences that can enhance our beliefs and values, and differences that are irreconcilable.

In conclusion, I wish to restate some guidelines for soul companioning inspired by Jean Stairs's contribution. First of all, the goal of a soul companion is to listen for the soul and the presence of God who is active in their lives.[15] Chaplains need to establish a rapport with the patient, listen for feelings, reflect feelings, express empathy, and identify spiritual issues that the care-receiver is concerned about. Chaplains do not need to take responsibility for the patient's religious (or non-religious) faith as such. They need to be attentive to how God is active in the patient's soul. Patients can take responsibility for their own beliefs. For example, in the verbatim presented above, Mrs. Wheatley was really concerned about missing the funeral. This was the cry of her grief touching her soul. She wanted to attend the funeral but could not be there due to her fractured ankle. The chaplain could have explored other ways in which she could bring closure and comfort to her brother-in-law's death that would be in keeping with her Jewish faith. The Jewish beliefs that are related to her grief are her responsibility, not the chaplain's. The chaplain is personally present to invite Mrs. Wheatley to reflect on her grief. The chaplain's responsibility is pastoral presence, understanding, and unconditional caring.

Secondly, Stairs reminds us that soul companioning affirms the com-

---

¹⁵ Stairs, *Listening For The Soul*, 142.

monality of our human experience.[16] Soul companioning can provide a way of coming together that rises above differences. In the verbatim above, both the chaplain and Mrs. Wheatley share the common human experience of grieving. We as a society are divided by social status, ethnic backgrounds, what neighborhoods we live in, financial incomes, and so on. There is enough that divides us, compartmentalizes us, isolates us. Grief becomes the common ground both the chaplain and Mrs. Wheatley can stand on with some comfort. In spiritual matters we can be present to one another in ways that bring clarity of meaning and new understanding that comes out of empathy. Soul companioning opens up the opportunity to make meaning out of one's spiritual crisis in a way that can be recognized, validated, and affirmed as a human experience elevated to a level of faith. If the patient is comfortable with his/her faith, he/she can validate the new spiritual meaning that develops out of the chaplain-patient relationship. It was unfortunate that the chaplain did not offer to include prayer in his ministry to Mrs. Wheatley.

Thirdly, Stairs states, "Soul companioning expands our spiritual vision and helps us cross boundaries."[17] "If someone says he loves God, but hates his brother, he is a liar. For he cannot love God, whom he has not seen, if he does not love his brother, whom he has seen" (1 John 4:20). Stairs points out that soul companioning challenges the chaplain to become more inclusive in a way that respects differences.[18] Chaplains are on a learning curve all the time. We are not experts, we are learners about how God interacts with us during crisis. Soul companioning provides an opportunity to learn truths beyond our awareness and to discover new meaning "outside of the box," if you will. It is a way to be aware of the truth that is beyond us, and that sometimes comes to us in a way we did not expect. The chaplain who ministered to Mrs. Wheatley might have discovered that by soul companioning Mrs. Wheatley in her grief, he would have learned more about how empowering the offer of hospitality can be. He would have learned something new in a way that is not threatening but truly revealing. When chaplains so respect the people they serve, they are likely to be more open to interfaith differences and, ultimately, more open to the very Spirit in whose name they serve.

---

[16] Ibid., 143.

[17] Ibid.

[18] Ibid.

Stepping into the borderlands
Prayer with people of different faiths

Leah Dawn Bueckert

When I was a child, our family owned a small, hardcover book entitled *Dolls from Many Lands*.[1] Each page of the book featured a drawing of a doll from a certain country along with a simple description of that culture. Pedro was from Mexico, Katrinka was from Holland, Vanya was from Russia, Luisa was from Argentina. According to my mother, by the time I was two or three years old I had memorized the names of each of the dolls and the countries they came from. My orientation to a positive view of diversity started young, in spite of the fact that I grew up in a predominantly Caucasian, middle class, Mennonite community. Since those early storybook days I have traveled overseas and have encountered people from a variety of cultures and faith traditions. My experiences in contexts where Caucasians were a *minority* have been relatively few and brief, but cultural diversity has been very much a part of my work, study, and friendship circles.

In this essay I offer a close look at three conversations I had as a resident chaplain with a Muslim man, two Hindu men, and a Jewish woman in the hospital. With these steps into the "borderlands" I hoped to play some part in the healing process. Somewhat awkward yet sincere, I initiated these encounters, guided by a conviction that I later found stated well by Peter Dula. In his essay, "A Theology of Interfaith Bridge Building," Dula emphasizes that borderlands can be places of growth and promise when we choose to *inhabit* them instead of fearing and avoiding

Leah Dawn Bueckert, M.Div., serves as Spiritual Care Coordinator with the North Eastman Health Association in Manitoba, Canada. She is based in the community of Beausejour, Manitoba.

[1] Written by Renee Bartkowkski, illustrated by Dorothy Grider (Chicago: Rand McNally & Co., 1975).

them.[2] He proceeds to reveal, through the lens of theologian Karl Barth, "that engaging persons of other faiths hospitably is an imperative for Christians."[3]

Sharing such hospitality may include praying with people of different faiths. Prayer is a common mode of expression for people from a variety of worldviews and traditions. Prayer is a way of articulating our deepest pain, deepest joy, greatest fears, greatest hopes, and our most closely held values. It is an acknowledgment of the limitations and deep longings of our human selves. Prayer is an act of faith in which the one praying decides to trust that care and healing are, or will be, somehow available.

Praying with people of different traditions is grounded in a Christian ethic of care. When their ministry is informed by an ethic of care,[4] chaplains serve patients and families as they would hope to be cared for themselves, while keeping in mind not to make assumptions based on their own preferences. They are attentive to the question: what does good news look like for this person? A Christian ethic of care is based on the biblical paradigm of shalom, namely, the integration of peace and justice that characterizes holistic well-being. In prayer we seek the realization of this well-being for individuals and for all of humanity. In the Judeo-Christian tradition, God understands the human plight as recounted during the Exodus journey of the Israelites and as seen in the life, death, and resurrection of Jesus. God promises to be a Companion in the midst of suffering, through the Holy Spirit. An ethic of care recognizes that human beings exist not in isolation but in relationships. We seek to support care receivers' experiences of right relationships. When a chaplain prays by drawing from the care receiver's own expressed needs and resources, evidence of a therapeutic relationship may well become a vehicle of grace and healing.

Extending welcome to care receivers of faiths different than ours may generate feelings of insecurity and anxiety. Questions about our own spiritual integrity may surface. We may feel uncomfortable if we are unfamiliar with certain cultural and religious traditions. While it is helpful and important to become more familiar with the customs and beliefs of diverse traditions, we must remember that people of any

---

[2] Peter Dula, "A Theology of Interfaith Bridge Building," in *Borders & Bridges: Mennonite Witness in a Religiously Diverse World,* edited by Peter Dula and Alain Epp Weaver (Telford: Cascadia Publishing House with Herald Press, 2007), 160–70.

[3] Ibid., 161.

[4] For a discussion of the "ethic of care" and its significance for a Christian understanding and practice of life and ministry see Leah Dawn Bueckert and Daniel S. Schipani, "The ethic of care in spiritual caregiving," in *Spiritual Caregiving in the Hospital: Windows to Chaplaincy Ministry* (Kitchener: Pandora Press, 2006), 233–44.

heritage—ourselves included—will have their own particular ways of interpreting and living the tradition. Our task is to learn how we might partner with them in drawing upon their values and beliefs in meaningful ways, whether they are religious or nonreligious. This may be easier said than done at times.

Often we can become perplexed even by people we know quite intimately. On the one hand, we may be able to guess how our spouse, friend or family member will respond to the events of life. On the other hand, we can still be surprised. Do we really know what goes on in their "heart of hearts"? Do they know what goes on in ours? How easy is it to fully express our sense of being loved or our experience of significant loss? These questions speak to a tension that is part of being human: the tension between familiarity and mystery. It is captured well by the following quote regarding the possibility of sharing religious experiences:

> We know from both hermeneutics as well as on the basis of our own personal experience that we cannot completely understand another person with regard to the most profound things.... Understanding what is going on in another person is not a question of 'all or nothing,' however.[5]

Meaningful encounters with people of other faiths require that we avoid the dichotomy demonstrated by the liberals' tendency towards superficial tolerance and the conservatives' tendency towards unreflective certitude—both at the expense of sincere engagement.[6] We aim beyond tolerance towards engagement and care, and beyond certitude towards admiration. By being candid about who we are as spiritual caregivers, and by being receptive to patients and families as they reveal who they are, we help build the trust and positive curiosity necessary for meaningful encounters.

A central feature of the role of spiritual caregivers is attentiveness to the stories of care receivers. As we invite patients and families to tell us about their lives, we begin to understand what they value and hold dear. By paying attention to these things we learn how to care for them, remembering that we glimpse the "tip of the iceberg." Amidst the expressed fears, hopes, and longings is the stuff that prayer is made of. In prayer we are always walking on holy ground.

---

[5] Jerald D. Gort, Hendrik M. Vroom, Rein Fernhout, & Anton Wessels, editors, *On Sharing Religious Experience: Possibilities of Interfaith Mutuality* (Grand Rapids: William B. Eerdmans, 1992), 5.

[6] Dula, "A Theology of Interfaith Bridge Building," 162.

When I first started as a chaplain I hesitated or neglected to offer spoken prayer because I did not want to come across as imposing my own faith practices. In my subsequent experiences I have been surprised by how frequently an offer to pray is welcomed by patients and families from diverse religious traditions as well as by those who identify themselves as nonreligious. In wondering about why this might be, I offer a few observations and hypotheses:

- Many people who do not affiliate with a religious community still pray or appreciate someone praying for them.

- Christianity has directly and indirectly shaped North American consciousness so that people may have a certain degree of familiarity (for better or worse) with what they will be receiving from me when they accept my offer to pray.

- Patients may not feel like they have the freedom to refuse the offer even if they would prefer to.

- The relationship that develops between the care receiver(s) and me is such that they feel they can trust that my motivation is one of care and not proselytism.

- People of diverse denominations or faith traditions hold the conviction that "there is one God."

- Members of cultural minorities that I encounter often seek to minimize the ways in which they feel marginalized by the society around them.

- Regardless of religious affiliation, people welcome prayer because it is a way of at least *trying* to give expression to "the most profound things" at a time of painful isolation. It may be a search for assurance that one's deepest needs will somehow be met in the midst of human limitation.

- Perhaps most important when it comes to sharing prayer, is the gift of knowing that one has been heard and cared for. When care receivers' own expressed concerns are woven into the chaplain's spoken prayer, their sense of isolation may be lessened and they may gain strength from knowing they have an ally in their healing process.[7]

---

[7] It is implied, of course, that caregivers must remember that not everyone will welcome prayer and the caregiver must respect this. Prayer is inappropriate when it stems from the chaplain's need to do so rather than from the development of the caregiving relationship and the patient's needs and spiritual resourcefulness.

These and other dynamics may be at play within care receivers when it comes to prayer. A Christian ethic of care motivates us in discerning whether or not to pray with patients and families of faith traditions and worldviews different than our own.[8]

This chapter focuses on prayer in three case studies that detail a few such interactions I had in the hospital. The cases are not meant to be "picture perfect" examples of how to conduct a visit in an interfaith situation. Rather, I offer them as accounts of conversations I actually had, including my weaker moments, for the sake of demonstrating what I learned from the experiences. Each of the vignettes is followed by a reflection on the nature of the visit. Positive outcomes of these situations are noted alongside observations about what could have been done better or differently. Group discussions with colleagues in pastoral care at Lutheran Hospital of Indiana informed some of these reflections.

Before proceeding with the cases, a few words about the cultural context that shapes me and my practice of spiritual caregiving will suffice as a preface to the three accounts. We all approach others through the lens of our own worldview, values, and assumptions. Awareness of our own biases and convictions should lead us to clarity about the guidelines behind our own practice of caregiving. In turn we are also reminded that the patients and families we serve are likewise shaped by their cultural contexts, values, and convictions.

My cultural context

Born in the 1970s to Mennonite parents, I grew up in a mid-sized prairie town in Manitoba, Canada. Mennonites from different conferences made up a large percentage of the population of my hometown. The word "Mennonite" is derived from the name Menno Simons, a Dutch Roman Catholic priest who became a leader in the sixteenth century Reformation/Anabaptist movement. One key feature of Anabaptist faith was expressed by another sixteenth century reformer, Hans Denck, who stated that the life of faith involves following Christ daily in life.[9] By following the example of Jesus, Mennonites believe we are called to extend

---

[8] For a helpful discussion on the value of praying with patients, see "The Use of Prayer" in Sharon Fish & Judith Allen Shelly, *Spiritual Care: The Nurse's Role* (Don Mills: InterVarsity Press, 1978), 95–106. This volume is written explicitly from a Christian perspective. The language is dated in terms of gender inclusiveness.

[9] Werner O. Packull, "Hans Denck: Fugitive from Dogmatism," in Hans-Juergen Goertz, ed., *Profiles of Radical Reformers: Biographical Sketches from Thomas Muenster to Paracelsus* (Scottdale: Herald Press, 1982), 62–71. See also W. Neff, "Denk (Denck), Hans," in *The Mennonite Encyclopedia*, vol. 2, Harold S. Bender and C. Henry Smith, editors (Scottdale: Mennonite Publishing House, 1956), 32–35.

hospitality *to* and accept hospitality *from* those within and outside our usual sphere of contact.

Another aspect of the Mennonite perspective, inspired by Jesus' own practice, is a commitment to nonviolent resistance in response to violence. Violence is a response primarily motivated by fear—fear of the unknown, fear of loss. Part of a Mennonite understanding of interfaith spiritual care includes the belief that building relationships with people from other traditions diminishes fear and violence.[10]

In addition to my theological formation, I also grew up alongside two interconnected socio-political phenomena: globalization and postmodernism. Increasingly, we live side by side with people from many different cultures. This has contributed to a growing awareness that the stories, customs, and traditions we live by influence the way we perceive each other and the world. In the years after I moved away from my hometown, I lived in North American neighborhoods that were much less homogenous than the one I came from. I encountered people whose beliefs and lifestyles were very different than mine.

We have a unique opportunity in the twenty-first century to welcome diversity in ways that transform threat into a sense of wonder and richness. This is easier said than done, however. Spiritual caregivers in the hospital face daily the challenge and responsibility to support the faith and hope of care receivers while ministering with integrity out of their own convictions and membership in a faith community. I, as a Mennonite, must be mindful of the theological convictions that guide my spiritual caregiving practice. What I believe affects, in every way, the kind of care I offer. At the same time, I must be willing to behold the world of those I care for and allow them to teach me, from the wisdom of their own experience. In so doing, I begin to learn how I might address their spiritual needs and partner with them in drawing upon their own resources.

Case 1: Nasim Hafeez[11]

Fifty-year-old Nasim Hafeez was taking time off from his work in construction to care for his eighty-year-old father. Mr. Hafeez, Sr., was an intensive care patient who had been admitted following a heart attack. While making rounds through intensive care, I caught Nasim's eye from where he sat beside the hospital bed. My first guess about his ethnicity

---

[10] For a summary of the Mennonite stance regarding nonviolence, see "Article 22: Peace, Justice, and Nonresistance" in *The Confession of Faith in a Mennonite Perspective* (Scottdale: Herald Press, 1995), 81–84.

[11] All names have been changed to protect the privacy of the people featured in the case studies.

was that perhaps he was from India. I said hello and introduced myself. Nasim invited me to enter the room. He told me his name and briefly related the events leading up to his father's hospitalization. Mr. Hafeez, Sr., was sedated and on a respirator, having gone through bypass surgery. Nasim looked concerned but calm.

"He is doing better," Nasim said with a hopeful tone. "He's on the respira-tor but he is really breathing on his own. They are probably going to take that tube out today."

"That sounds like good news," I said.

"Yes, he's doing okay. He had a heart attack and they had to do bypass surgery. He is always very active and healthy."

"He stays in good shape."

"Yes. That's why this was a surprise. He is strong, so he will get better."

"And you are able to take the time to be here?"

"Yes. I am here every day. My brother comes too. He lives with my brother. He'll be coming soon," Nasim paused then said, "My mother died in this hospital."

"Oh, she did?"

"Yes, she had a stroke. She was here for a few weeks. There was too much blood on her brain. We were here then, too."

A respiratory technologist, along with two students, wheeled into the room with his computer and indicated that they were going to do a test to determine if Mr. Hafeez was ready to be weaned off of the respirator. He addressed Nasim and said they would need him to translate. It took a few minutes for them to get set up. Nasim told me that his father spoke Urdu.

"Say a prayer for him?" Nasim requested, nodding over at his father.

I agreed and we bowed our heads while the respiratory team made prepara-tions. "God of life and love, we ask for your blessing upon Mr. Hafeez. We give you thanks for the healing that is already happening since his surgery and pray that you will continue to work through the hands of the nurses and doctors and other staff here at the hospital, restoring Mr. Hafeez in body, soul, and spirit. May he know of your care also through the support of his family and friends; we thank you for his sons who are here with him. In your grace and mercy, hear our prayer. Amen."

After the prayer, the respiratory technologist began. He had Nasim tell his father to take a few deep breaths and blow out as hard as he could. The technologist measured his breathing and made positive comments about the situation. Within ten minutes the test was done and Nasim was told that the doctor would be in to confirm the next steps.

"Sounds like your father did well, according to the technologist."

"Yes. We'll see what the doctor says."

"Yes," I paused, "Is there anything you need right now?"

"No. I am fine. Thank you. How long have *you* been here?"

"Almost a year."

"And are you a minister?"

"I am a chaplain with the hospital full time and I worship with a Mennonite Church."

"Oh yes. I know the Mennonites."

"And you? Is there a faith community you belong to?"

"We are Muslim. But we are all God's children."

"Yes. We are all loved by the same God."

"Yes. There are so many stereotypes about what Muslims are like. But it is a political Islam that people see—the political Islam is not the true Islam. We pray in the name of Jesus."

"You do?"

"Yes!"

"I didn't know that."

"Many people do not know that, but we do. We believe that Jesus was the Son of God. Jesus did not have a human father. Mohammad did. So Jesus is the Son of God. There are Muslims who will not say that. But nobody can speak against Jesus. In Pakistan, if anyone says anything against Jesus or Abraham or Mohammad, they can be sent to jail."

"Really."

"Yes. There are laws governing what people can say," Nasim paused, "I know the Mennonites. I work in construction and there are Mennonites who work with me. Right now we are building a mosque together."

"Oh, you are? What do your Mennonite co-workers say about that?"

"They say, 'Jews, Christians, and Muslims all share the same God.' The

Jews believe from Abraham up until Jesus—they don't believe Jesus is the Son of God. Christians believe from Abraham up until Mohammad—they say it stops with Jesus. From the time of Abraham, every prophet was told about who would come next. Jesus received a revelation about Mohammad. That is what we believe."

"Well I appreciate your sharing about it. I have learned some things I did not know before! When we live and work side by side with people of different faiths it is good when we can get to know each other."

"Yes. I enjoy working with the Mennonites."

The cardiologist entered the room to speak with Nasim.

"Mr. Hafeez, I will be on my way," I said, extending my hand to him and he shook it. "It was good to meet you."

"Thank you. If you ever want to stop by and say a prayer for my father, you are most welcome to."

"Thank you. I will do that. Bye."

It is clear that I was graciously received by Nasim Hafeez. Two significant matters surface in this encounter. First, Nasim was confronting the possible loss of someone he loves. Second, he was experiencing this as a Muslim in a Christian context at a time of vulnerability. All of us experience death and loss as part of the human condition. Beyond this common ground, however, each situation is unique and it is important to respect cultural and religious differences. Nasim needed assurance that his father would receive the best care possible; he also needed to know that he would be respected even though his religious convictions were different, in some significant ways, than those of most of the staff at the hospital. As he kept vigil with his father, who was hanging in the balance between life and death, Nasim also needed the freedom to draw upon his faith as a source of strength and hope.

My purpose as chaplain in this encounter was to offer spiritual support by listening and praying, as requested, and by exploring Nasim's faith as a source of nurture and guidance. With his request for a prayer early in the visit he expressed a desire to make supplication to God for his father's recovery. He made this request before he knew anything about me other than my being a Christian spiritual caregiver, symbolized by the cross on my navy blazer. I did not know his religious background, if any, at that point and, therefore, I intentionally refrained from using the words "in Jesus' name" to close the prayer. Our subsequent conversation revealed that he personally, though he was a Muslim, would not have been offended if I had prayed in Jesus' name in his presence.[12]

Regardless of how much we know about any religious tradition, this encounter demonstrates that every person within that tradition will have a unique way of interpreting the connection between their spirituality and their life circumstances.[13] I maintain that it is important for spiritual caregivers to make decisions about the religious language we use based on our fullest understanding of what would be meaningful for the people in our care in that moment.[14] I do not need to audibly pray the words "in Jesus' name" as if the prayer is incomplete without them. As a Christian, my prayers are always in Jesus' name, whether or not I explicitly say the words.[15] I pray those words explicitly when I am with people whose faith and worldview are similar to mine because we are more likely to share an understanding about why those words are meaningful. In this particular conversation with Nasim I would like to have asked, in retrospect, about his own experience of prayer.[16]

If I had asked Nasim more about his mother's death in this same hospital, we might have talked about what gave him hope in the midst of that experience. We might have talked about that time in light of Nasim's father, now on a respirator. Experiences with mortality, grief, hope, and love are fundamentally human. We are all dependent and interdependent, regardless of religious affiliation. At the same time, religious distinctions

---

[12] It is important to keep in mind, of course, that praying "in the name of Jesus" may mean something very different to a Muslim than to a Christian.

[13] For a helpful discussion about learning from the patient see Elizabeth Johnston Taylor, *What Do I Say? Talking with patients about spirituality* (Philadelphia: Templeton Foundation Press, 2007), 111.

[14] For a discussion of this challenge see Leah Dawn Bueckert and Daniel S. Schipani, "Interfaith Spiritual Caregiving: The Case for Language Care," in Bueckert and Schipani, editors, *Spiritual Caregiving in the Hospital*, 245–63.

[15] For me to pray in Jesus' name stems from my belief that God was uniquely present in Jesus of Nazareth—in his care for the sick, the suffering and the outcast, in his non-violent and wise challenge of the powers of domination. When I pray in Jesus' name, I ask that God's will be done as seen in the life and faith, death and resurrection of Jesus who sought redemption and healing for all.

[16] One of the "Five Pillars of Faith" in Muslim tradition is to pray five times a day, accompanied by ritual cleansing. It is important for caregivers to help make this possible, according to the abilities of the patient, by providing a pitcher of water and a basin to wash with, for example. Prayers emphasize praise of Allah Most Compassionate, Most Merciful instead of personal requests, as the latter could be considered criticism of Allah's will for the person praying. Following is an example of a prayer that might be offered. "O Allah, Lord of the people, remove all harm, give care, for you are the one who cures. There is not curing except your curing—a curing that leaves no illness. (Bukhari)." Mary M. Toole *Handbook for Chaplains: Comfort My People* (New York: Paulist Press, 2006), 23–9. See also Neville A. Kirkwood, *A Hospital Handbook on Multiculturalism and Religion: Practical Guidelines for Health Care Workers*, revised edition (Harrisburg: Morehouse Publishing, 2005), 28–40.

regarding these experiences are very significant and must be taken into consideration.

I understood that Nasim communicated some sadness and anger about some people's perception of him as a Muslim. Perhaps the source of these feelings came from life in North America amidst a prevailing negative attitude towards Muslims. Had I been more aware of the possible reasons why Nasim was showing interest in establishing common ground, such as expressing the right to be treated with respect as a "visible minority," I could have been more conscious to be an advocate for him with other hospital staff. I might have done this by asking Nasim how he was experiencing the staff's treatment of him and his father and if there were things being overlooked in relation to the customs of his family and tradition. I could also have asked if he was affiliated with a particular mosque or worshipping community and, if so, whether or not this was a support to him at this time. I wanted him to have the assurance that we as staff would work together with him to provide care that would respect his faith and culture. I hoped that, through our encounter, Nasim had a sense of being heard and cared for. My motivation was for the sustaining power of his faith to be enhanced during our visit and throughout this difficult time.

Case 2: Tarak Ajit Maruti

Tarak Ajit was a 43-year-old Hindu man. He was being treated on the neuro-medical surgical unit following a stroke. Originally from India, he was currently living in Indiana. I had visited Tarak once before but, because of the language challenge, we had some trouble communicating. When I looked into the room this time, another man was with him. Tarak was lying in bed with the head of the bed slightly raised. He was in a single room; the window blinds were open. The visitor was standing at the foot of the bed. During our conversation I learned that this man was Tarak's friend Peter, also from India but having lived in the United States for a longer period of time. He was fluent in both Hindi and English.

"How have you been since the last time we talked?" I asked. Tarak responded with a question mark on his face. I started again, "How are you?"

"Fine," he answered.

"Have you been doing exercises?" I inquired, trying to open a conversation that connected with the first time I met him. Peter interpreted my question.

"Yes," Tarak answered affirmatively.

"In the mornings," Peter added.

"What kind of exercises do you do?" Peter again interpreted my question. Tarak began to lift his left arm up and down with his right hand. "Arm exercises. And walking?"

Peter answered, "He uses a walker and somebody supports his left side."

"Are you here when he does his exercises?" I asked Peter.

"No, I'm not here in the morning."

"How did the two of you meet?" I asked.

"We come from the same place in India and we have the same last name."

"Oh really? But you met here in Indiana?"

"Yes. A friend of his is also my friend and so we met. I am looking for a job and I heard that he was in the hospital. So I came here to be with him—I like to be here when he needs help."

Turning to Tarak I said, "Good to have friends, isn't it?" Tarak nodded. "Last time we talked you told me that you are Hindu."

"Yes," Tarak replied.

"As a Christian, I'm interested to know more about what it is like to be Hindu." Tarak smiled and nodded. "It must be different to be here in Indiana where there aren't very many people who are Hindu—different than in India where, what, 70 percent of the population is Hindu?"

"In India?" Peter asked.

"Yes."

"Oh, about 80 percent are Hindu, 13 percent are Muslim, and the rest are Christian and others."

"Oh, I see," I said. "That must be a different experience."

"Yes. It's different." Peter replied, "but I go into a church."

"A Christian church?"

"Yes. There is one God. Whether I am in a temple or in a mosque or in a church—Krishna, Rama, Jesus—it's all the same God."

"Different names for one God," I said.

"Yes—different names for one God. That's what *I* believe."

"What about you?" I asked, looking at Tarak. Peter interpreted my question.

Pointing up with his finger Tarak said, "One God."

"I also believe that." I stated. "Do you also pray in the Hindu tradition?"

Peter interpreted and then said, "Yes, we pray."

"What is it like for you to pray? How do you pray?" Peter chuckled and interpreted for Tarak. Tarak put his hands together and bowed his head.

"Do you know what he is saying?" Peter asked me. "He is saying when we go into the temple we stand in front of the god, we put our hands together—like you—and bow our head—the same. In a temple there is a statue, in a mosque there may be nothing, in a Christian church there is a statue of Jesus. The method doesn't matter, it's what is in the heart that's important."

"Yes, God knows the heart." I replied. Looking at Tarak I asked, "What do you pray for?" Peter interpreted and Tarak touched his arm, looking at me.

"For health, for the body to be restored." I said.

Peter added, "For strength in his leg and his arm so that he can go back to India."

"Yes of course." I said. "To recover and be well again; to go home."

Peter returned to the subject of God. "Human is the same everywhere—one God. But not everyone believes that. If everyone believed that, the world would be very different, I think. Now there is always fighting."

"Yes, it seems that our differences sometimes get in the way." Looking at Tarak, I asked, "Would it be all right if I say a prayer with you?"

Peter interpreted the question and then said, "That would be all right." He interpreted to Tarak as I prayed, line by line.

"O God who loves us all, thank you for the opportunity to talk with Peter and Tarak. As Tarak spends these days in the hospital, we pray that your healing will strengthen his body and that your spirit of peace would bless him. Thank you for the friendship that Tarak and Peter share. Thank you for the care of the medical staff here. Give the staff guidance and wisdom. We pray that Tarak will regain his strength day by day. We pray that he will soon be able to return home to India. May Tarak know your love and healing through the care of those around him. Amen."

After exchanging a few more words, I thanked them for the visit and we said good-bye.

One of the most obvious features of many intercultural and interfaith encounters is the difference in spoken language. Even the basics of everyday communication become a challenge. Nonverbal language communicates up to a point, but verbal language allows for the clarification of needs and confirmation of meaning.[17]

Tarak was in a vulnerable condition in the hospital of a foreign culture. According to my assumptions and our conversation, Tarak was counting on compassionate and competent medical care. He needed to experience respect for his cultural and religious preferences and to have a mediator between the Western culture of the hospital and his own context. Peter was a friend and caregiver in these and other respects.

For my part, I could have learned a little more about Tarak as a person rather than asking straight out about his being Hindu. I could have asked, "Do you have a place of worship here in Indiana?" or, "What gives you hope at a time like this?"[18]

My asking so brashly about their Hindu faith may have given the message that I was there to educate myself rather than to be attentive to their needs. I continue to remind myself that my own curiosity does not always have a place—I must learn to distinguish between "good" curiosity and simple nosiness.

Peter mentioned early on that he had been to a church. When I asked, somewhat puzzled, "to a Christian church?" he responded affirmatively. Much like Nasim conveyed his familiarity with Christianity, Peter's comments also seem to suggest a desire to minimize the differences between us. By *pointing* to the differences, I intended to communicate openness to learning about their culture and traditions, but I wonder if this rather had the effect of emphasizing the barriers between us. Whatever the case, they certainly extended hospitality to *me*.

Peter said, "There is one God—Krishna, Rama, Jesus—it is all the

---

[17] Had Peter not been present, I would have asked my colleague who was fluent in Hindi to accompany me on this visit. Resources such as an interpreter phone line are also available in some places. Such arrangements are fundamental to the communication of respect. They allow us to hear the patient's own expressed hopes and to build towards a therapeutic relationship.

[18] According to Mary M. Toole in *Handbook for Chaplains*, Hindu worship practices are not possible in the hospital. For this reason, the patient's family will conduct practices at home or at the temple. "As a greeting, Hindus join hands at the palms and bow from the waist saying *Namaskar* or *Namaste*, which means 'I bow to God in you; I love you and I respect you, as there is no one like you." Following is one example of a Vedic prayer: "O! All powerful God. You are the protector of the whole physical creation. May you protect my body. You art the source of all life. You art the source of all strength. Make thou me strong. O, omnipotent Lord, I live to thee to fill up all my wants and to give me perfection, physical, mental and spiritual." Toole, *Handbook for Chaplains*, 15–22. See also Kirkwood, *A Hospital Handbook on Multiculturalism and Religion*, 54–63.

same God." My reply to Peter's comment was an affirmative one: "Different names for one God." Why would I, as a Christian, make a response like this? My answer has two parts. First, I interpreted Peter's words as a statement about the dependence of human beings upon God and not as an invitation to a discussion about doctrine. Second and more to the point, while there are, of course, significant distinctions between Hindu faith and Christian faith, we know that Christianity cannot stop truth from existing outside of it. In fact, according to Peter Dula on Karl Barth, the church's constant temptation will be to insulate itself from the world when it is often the prophetic word from outside that promises to be the source of growth and transformation. Dula writes:

> To commit oneself to the practice of interfaith bridge building is to presume, with Barth, that there are true lights and words in other religions. The point of interfaith bridge building is to see and listen to these true lights and words … . Attending to other words and lights is, on Barth's grounds, the way to focus on Christ.[19]

In other words, for the Christian, any true word that is found "outside" of Christianity, will be a reflection and confirmation of the one Word. The *Confession of Faith in a Mennonite Perspective* states:

> We humbly recognize that God far surpasses human comprehension and understanding. We also gratefully acknowledge that God has spoken to humanity and related to us in many and various ways. We believe that God has spoken above all in the only Son, the Word who became flesh and revealed the divine being and character.[20]

In light of Biblical foundations, on the one hand, God is beyond all human description. On the other hand, God is truly knowable through revelation. In the Christian tradition God is revealed more fully than anywhere else in the person of Jesus Christ. If there are, then, any ways in which Rama or Krishna reflect the light of Jesus Christ, "it is all the same God."

I have a rudimentary awareness of the Hindu tradition—enough to

---

[19] Dula, "A Theology of Interfaith Bridge Building," 165.

[20] "Article 1: God," in *Confession of Faith in a Mennonite Perspective* (Scottdale: Herald Press, 1995), 10, 11. Scripture references upon which these statements are based: Exodus 3:13–14; Job 37; Isaiah 40:18–25; Romans 11:33–36; John 1:14, 18; Hebrews 1:1–4.

appreciate that there are similarities as well as significant distinctions between it and Christianity.[21] My commitment to the convictions of my own faith community does not give me license to make assumptions about the right-ness or wrong-ness of others' beliefs. Like the parable of the householder who did not trust the servants to preserve the wheat while pulling out the weeds, so too I must be careful about the judgments and assumptions I make about people from other traditions and their faith commitments.[22] What seems wrong to me in someone else may not necessarily be so. Peter Dula states it sharply when he writes:

> Barth is not saying that all we have to do is glance around and see what words are or are not reflecting the Word and then pay close patient attention to them. His whole point is that, given an awareness of our sinfulness, we will likely not be able to recognize, or will misrecognize, those words when we do see them.[23]

Our good intentions coupled with our human tendency to deceive ourselves can result in prejudice and discrimination of various kinds. We do, of course, make judgment calls based on our values and beliefs, and we must. We *should* act to promote what is life-giving and healing and work against oppression and violence. What the quote above highlights is the need to maintain a measure of humility in our judgments, recognizing that it is God in the end who is judge.

As Christian spiritual caregivers in health care settings, our role is to extend hospitality, to step into the borderlands between faith traditions and hospital culture, and to embody the love we believe in. While I did not fully understand what goes on within Peter and Tarak in regards to "the most profound things," I did learn that they have faith in a God upon whom they depend for life and well-being. In my prayer with them I addressed the "God who loves us all". May I continue to learn what it means to point to the God who is truly knowable and to humble myself

---

[21] Hindu deities represent different aspects of the one Supreme Being or God. The cosmic activity of the Supreme Being is characterized by three tasks: creation, preservation, and dissolution and recreation. Brahma represents the activity of creation, Vishnu represents preservation, and Shiva represents the work of dissolution and recreation. Rama and Krishna are the seventh and eighth incarnations of Vishnu. Rama represents an ideal man. Krishna, the flute player, is seen as the fullest representation of Vishnu. See C. J. Fuller, *The Camphor Flame: Popular Hinduism and Society in India* (Princeton: Princeton University Press, 1992), 29–56 and J. L. Brockington, *The Sacred Thread: A Short History of Hinduism* (Delhi: Oxford University Press, 1992).

[22] Matthew 13:24–30.

[23] Dula, "A Theology of Interfaith Bridge Building," 168.

before the same God who is truly mysterious.

Case 3: Megan Blomstein

While making rounds on cardiac telemetry, I stopped in the room of a 57-year-old woman named Megan. After introducing myself to Megan and three family members, I asked how she was feeling. She described what it was like to be recovering from a heart attack. Her husband also volunteered thoughts about his own recent experience of being hospitalized. After we had been conversing for awhile, I was about to offer a prayer, but before doing so, I asked:

"Are you part of a church community?"

"We're Jewish," Megan replied.

"Oh, you are."

"We go to synagogue, to one of the two synagogues here in town."

"Are they aware that you are in the hospital?"

"Yes, the Rabbi has been here."

"I don't encounter people from the Jewish tradition here very often. What is it like to be at a Lutheran hospital?"

"Oh, the staff have been wonderful. We have both received really good care here. The only thing I don't like is when people come to proselytize."

"Yes, that's not helpful."

"Something kind of funny happened the other day. A woman from dietary was here and I wanted to let her know that I did not want to be served anything with pork. There was no place to mark my request on her form, so she said, 'Well, we'll have to write it under food allergies!'"

We chuckled. "Hmm," I said, "It sounds like we need to revise those forms."[24]

Megan quickly responded, "We've been very happy with the care we've received here. My doctor is excellent."

"I am glad to hear that you feel you've been treated well. May that continue. I know Jews and Christians pray differently, but I ..."

Before I could finish, Megan said, "If you would like to pray in the name of God, that would be wonderful."

---

[24] I pursued this matter with dietary staff who suggested that the best place for requests like this on the meal order forms would be in the "staff notes" section. While the hospital kitchen is not a kosher kitchen, I was told they do offer some kosher foods.

"Okay. I would be glad to." After a short pause for centering, I prayed: "God of grace and love, thank you for the opportunity to meet with Megan and her family. As she spends these days in the hospital, may she continue to know your loving care for her through the care of the medical staff and through the support of family and friends. May your healing touch restore her in body, soul, and spirit. Grant her your mercy and peace throughout the rest of this day and in the coming days. Amen."

"Thank you."

"You're welcome," I said and bid them farewell.

Megan and her family, even though they had experienced the irritation of having others attempt to proselytize in the past, were patient with me, a Christian chaplain who rather clumsily sought to communicate respect and care. This conversation seems to have had two notable features; Megan affirmed the good care she had received on the one hand, while expressing frustration, with humor, over experiences with religious insensitivity on the other hand.

After they shared with me that they were Jewish and were affiliated with a local synagogue, I sought to remain engaged, at least for a little while, instead of withdrawing and assuming this meant the termination of the visit. Withdrawal would have been easier. It would have been easier to act as if my task as a chaplain (to be a blessing and to address any spiritual needs) was irrelevant in the face of these discovered religious differences. As a spiritual caregiver, the fact that they were Jewish needed to *inform and guide* my role with them, not make my role irrelevant. It is possible, however, that my sense of being caught a little off guard hindered my ability to interact in a relaxed and non-threatening manner. For example, my response to Megan's statement about people coming to proselytize communicated a closing of my interest instead of an opening. Looking back, I wonder if Megan wasn't wary throughout our visit about where this conversation was going.

Earlier in the visit, I had stated that I don't encounter people of Jewish faith very often and could they tell me what the hospital experience was like for them. My intention in making this comment was to convey an interest in learning how we might be helpful. I wanted to communicate that I was not about to impose my "Christian services." My intentions were good. I'm not so sure that my words had the desired effect. First of all, as with Tarak, my statement accentuated their being different in a context where they deserved to be assured that they would be treated with the same respect and quality as everyone else. Second, by asking them to tell me what it is like to be Jewish in a "Christian" hospital, I may have sounded as if I was using them to educate myself instead of focusing on them and their needs. As spiritual caregivers we do have a responsibility to regard the care receiver as the expert on their own experience. The hope is to communicate respect and appreciation, not a self-interested agenda about my own learning.

Instead of saying, "I don't encounter people from the Jewish tradition very often; tell me what it's like for you here at the hospital," I could have said, "I'm glad to hear that you've been happy with the care you've received. Is there anything that has been frustrating or overlooked?" This would have been a better way to communicate a desire to be of service. After Megan spoke about her irritation when people come to proselytize, I could have said, "Tell me more about that." This might have created an opportunity to address the connection between her faith and her current experience.

Megan seemed to sense my offer to pray coming. I wonder whether she really felt okay with me praying, or if she felt exasperated and thought to herself, "If she's going to insist on praying, I will at least direct the terms." If Megan was irritated by my praying with her, then my actions were a misuse of my role and position in the hospital system. If she was truly extending the invitation, then my actions may have been a channel for the light and love of God. Instead of my comment, "I know Jews and Christians pray differently," perhaps I could have said, "I would like to offer a blessing for your recovery." Or perhaps I should not have prayed at all. Some would say it is inappropriate for a Jew and a Christian to pray together. Perhaps the most respect I could have shown would have been to *not* offer to pray. I might have said that I would pray *for* them. Or my parting words might have served as a sort of blessing. [25]

It is not necessary to include a prayer for a spiritual care visit to be of value, but *if the care receiver finds it meaningful*, it can be a powerful reminder of grace, connection, and hope, for both care receiver and care-giver. The challenge is to determine whether or not the receiver would sincerely welcome prayer. We can say it is up to patients to refuse, but in their compromised position, will they feel free to say no? With Megan I

---

[25] See Chapter 5 in this book, "A Chaplain Reflects on Caring for a Jewish Family," by William H. Griffith. In this essay the chaplain forms his blessing by drawing upon texts that he and the family had in common, in this case, the Psalms and Deuteronomy.

There are four movements within Judaism. They are Orthodox, Reform, Conservative, and Reconstructionist. Most synagogues are affiliated with one of these. Kirkwood writes, "Jewish prayer embraces elements of petition, thanksgiving, praise, confession, sustaining and healing"

have lingering uncertainty about that. By contrast, in the meetings with Nasim, Tarak, and Peter, the receivers clearly welcomed and, in Nasim's case, requested prayer.

Welcome of the stranger is a common theme throughout the Hebrew Bible and the Gospels of Jesus, as highlighted in several places in this book.[26] Megan and her family did show grace and hospitality throughout our interaction. I hope I showed hospitality by attempting to express respect and a desire to learn how to relate to them as a chaplain.

In conclusion, it was a privilege for me to spend time with each of these people—Nasim, Tarak, Peter, and Megan. I have learned much and will continue to learn from these encounters, these steps into the borderlands. As Christian spiritual caregivers in a multifaith milieu, it is not only our *professional* and *ethical* responsibility to engage people of other faiths with openness and respect, it is our *theological* and *pastoral* responsibility as well. In the words of Alain Epp Weaver, "we engage in interfaith bridge-building *because*, not in spite, of our Christological convictions."[27] While the subject of Christology requires another discussion, suffice it to say that Jesus' life and ministry, death and resurrection portray indiscriminate love in word and action. That is why our convictions free us for boundless compassion.

Engaging in interfaith spiritual caregiving, therefore, does not require that we give up our convictions, though they may be challenged. Neither is it an attempt to find merely a politically correct or "lowest common denominator" level of relating. It means that we open ourselves to the discomfort of interacting with people who present much to us that is unfamiliar. It means that we take the time to listen long and deeply. If appropriate and solicited, we may share about our own faith. If there is disagreement, we continue to maintain positive regard for the other person. If we detect that those we care for are somehow misguided we probe gently, directed by compassion, maintaining the possibility that we may be wrong or have something to learn. Interfaith bridge-building

---

(43). Toole includes this Jewish prayer: "Heal us, O Lord, and we shall be healed, save us and we shall be saved; for You are our glory. Grant complete healing for all our afflictions, faithful and merciful God of healing" (37). Mary M. Toole *Handbook for Chaplains*, 33–43. See also Neville A. Kirkwood, *A Hospital Handbook on Multiculturalism and Religion*, 41–53.

[26] For example, see the Preface and Chapter 4, "Biblical Foundations: Challenges and Possibilities of Interfaith Caregiving," by Daniel Schipani.

[27] Alain Epp Weaver, "Interfaith Bridge Building in the Middle East," in *Mennonite Central Committee Peace Office Newsletter: Interfaith Bridge Building*, vol. 35, no. 4 (October–December 2005), 6, 7.

calls us to cultivate and deepen our own spiritual wellsprings. Again, it is precisely by realizing the wideness of God's mercy, as demonstrated by Christ, that we are freed to extend hospitality to people we meet from other traditions.

From a clinical perspective, sharing prayer with someone of another faith tradition can be a meaningful bridge-building experience.[28] From a pastoral theological perspective, that practice is grounded in a Christian ethic of care. When patients and families remark that "there is one God," they are expressing, among other things, our common human dependence upon that which is beyond us. Death and loss are universally human experiences; we are not, ultimately, in control of the length of our days. We may, however, encourage one another as we glimpse, work towards, and wait for the full integration of justice and peace on earth.

As a Christian, my understanding of God and life is different in many ways from Islamic, Hindu, or Jewish understandings. On what basis, then, do I pray together with someone of another faith, once I've confirmed that that person desires prayer? First, Christians recognize that God is beyond comprehension. The God of mystery calls us to trust and to refrain from judgment. Second, Christians profess that God is knowable and revealed through Scripture and especially in Jesus. The God of incarnation calls us to compassion. Prayer is one way to give voice to pain, joy, fear, and hope. When making intercession for a patient or family in such a way that our words mirror their own expressed concerns, we communicate that we have heard them and that we want to be partners with them and the Holy Spirit in the healing process. As we step into the borderlands and open ourselves to each other, we discover the Divine is already there in our midst.

---

[28] For a thoughtful list on "Tips for praying with patients," see Johnston Taylor, *What Do I Say? Talking with Patients About Spirituality*, 98–100.

Part 2

**Bases for a theological framework
for interfaith care**

Biblical foundations

Challenges and possibilities of interfaith caregiving

Daniel S. Schipani

Pastoral theological reflection on the practice of caregiving must always include sound biblical-theological dimensions. As already noted in the previous chapters, interfaith spiritual care elicits a number of hermeneutical and theological questions that need to be addressed. This essay illustrates the responsibility pastoral caregivers have to carefully interpret and appropriate biblical material in light of the plurality of traditions represented in Scripture. This is, indeed, the case given the tension between exclusiveness and inclusiveness apparent in both Testaments, in Christian theology in general, and in denominational "confessions of faith" in particular. It is our assumption that interfaith spiritual care from a Christian theological perspective can and must be biblically grounded.

Our hermeneutical key is the normative testimony of Jesus' own faith, life, and ministry. The fundamental theological claim we make in light of that testimony consists in the affirmation of the unfathomable reach, inclusiveness, and availability of Grace. For that reason, we will focus on a window to Jesus' own existential and vocational struggle as a caregiver in a reported encounter with a stranger in the borderlands. The appendix presents a summary of selected Old and New Testament sources which can be considered to undergird spiritual care in interfaith situations from a pastoral theological perspective.

A study of Matthew 15:21–28 as paradigmatic story[1]

Throughout the centuries, Christians have interpreted and used the story

Daniel S. Schipani, Dr.Psy., Ph.D., is an ordained minister of the Mennonite Church. He is Professor of Pastoral Care and Counseling at the Associated Mennonite Biblical Seminary, Elkhart, Indiana.

[1] What follows is a revised and expanded version of my article, "Transformation in the Borderlands: A Study of Matthew 15:21–28," in *Vision: A Journal for Church and Theology*, vol. 2, no. 2 (Fall 2001), 13–24.

of Jesus' encounter with the Syrophoenician/Canaanite woman in many ways. In recent years writings from a variety of perspectives reflect renewed interest in this fascinating story.[2] Working with a practical theological perspective, I will address two interrelated questions: how might this biblical text become foundational for caregiving ministry?[3] How might this unique story further illumine the challenges and opportunities of intercultural and interfaith care for Christian caregivers?

I will follow the familiar movements of an inductive study process, in popularized Latin American terms: *seeing, judging,* and *acting.* First, we will take a close look at the biblical passage, trying to grasp its meaning afresh. Second, we will ponder its significance, keeping in mind the social and cultural context. Finally, we will draw implications for our embodiment of the message in truthful and fruitful ways.

The meaning of the text: *Seeing*

This story appears only in the Gospels according to Mark and Matthew. In fact, Mark chapter 7 and Matthew chapter 15 are remarkably parallel as far as narrative content and sequencing are concerned. Nevertheless, we note some significant differences between the two accounts of Jesus' encounter with a foreign woman.[4] These dissimilarities suggest that Matthew has an interest in underscoring and intensifying some features of the story. For this reason, I have chosen to focus on its narrative.

> Jesus left that place and went away to the district of Tyre and Sidon. Just then a Canaanite woman from that

---

[2] Elisabeth Schüssler Fiorenza took the title of her book, *But She Said: Feminist Practices of Biblical Interpretation* (Boston: Beacon Press, 1992), from the story of the Syrophoenician-Canaanite woman. In her view, the story "represents the biblical-theological voice of women, which has been excluded, repressed, or marginalized in Christian discourse" (11).

[3] As a practical theologian, I use the term "foundational" deliberately and precisely. For me, the Bible is foundational in at least four interrelated ways: (a) It informs my normative framework and perspective for practice and reflection, especially regarding wisdom (knowing how to live in the light of God); (b) it offers key content disclosed in the teachings, narratives, and other materials (poetic, prophetic, apocalyptic, etc.) which express the written Word in ways that illumine and address our human condition; (c) it calls for engagement in an interpretive process for the sake of discernment and wise living; and (d) it grounds my own spirituality as a man of faith and as a ministering person (pastoral counselor and pastoral care supervisor), theological educator, and theologian.

[4] One is inclined to think that the narrative would also fit well in Luke's Gospel, given what we know about Luke, a Gentile writing to Gentiles, who gives women a significant place in his telling of the gospel. According to Elisabeth Schüssler Fiorenza, Luke does not include the story because he puts Paul and Peter at the center of the debate about the mission to the Gentiles: "This Lukan historical model has no room for a story about an educated Greek woman, who as a religious and ethnic outsider argues with Jesus for the Gentiles' share in the power of well-being" (Fiorenza, *But She Said*, 97).

region came out and started shouting, "Have mercy on
me, Lord, Son of David; my daughter is tormented by a
demon." But he did not answer her at all. And his disciples came and urged him, saying, "Send her away, for
she keeps shouting after us." He answered, "I was sent
only to the lost sheep of the house of Israel." But she
came and knelt before him, saying, "Lord, help me." He
answered, "It is not fair to take the children's food and
throw it to the dogs." She said, "Yes, Lord, yet even the
dogs eat the crumbs that fall from their masters' table."
Then Jesus answered her, "Woman, great is your faith!
Let it be done for you as you wish." And her daughter
was healed instantly. (Matthew 15:21–28, NRSV)

Our story is placed in a particular context in both Matthew 15 and
Mark 7. First, we learn about a serious controversy involving Pharisees
and scribes concerning the "tradition of the elders" on the question of
eating with defiled hands. Jesus responds by accusing them of breaking the
commandment of God and making void the word of God for the sake of
their tradition, including a damning quote from the prophet Isaiah (Mt
15:1–9, Mk 7:1–13). Then we are told that Jesus engages in authoritative
teaching about the spiritual implications of his position. In fact, he does
this by using both direct and indirect language, that is, parabolic communication that requires further explanation (Mt 15:10–20, Mk 7:14–23).
Finally, after the story of the encounter with the Syrophoenician/Canaan-
ite woman, the Gospel writers portray Jesus involved in ministry with
admirable compassion and power (Mt 15:29–39, Mk 7:31–37).

It is significant that, before encountering the foreign woman, Jesus
has been engaged in a very serious conflict situation. His adversaries put
the controversy in terms of socio-religious, cultural adaptation, that is,
the conventional wisdom of needing to follow the tradition of the elders.
In other words, the Gospel accounts suggest that the nature of their
argument betrays a two-dimensional vision: they understand holiness in
terms of conformity to the precepts and practices handed down through
religious teachings and socialization. Observance of the tradition, then,
defines one's belonging to the chosen people of Israel. Jesus, on the other
hand, views the struggle four-dimensionally:[5] for him, the real problem

---

[5] This is a direct allusion to James E. Loder's view of the "fourfold knowing event"—which
involves the lived world, the self, the void, and the Holy. See *The Transforming Moment*, 2nd ed.
(Colorado Springs: Helmers & Howard, 1989), chapter 3. Loder writes that "being human entails

lies in accommodating tradition while disobeying the will of God, as in the case of the commandment to honor father and mother. In that light, Jesus contends that the very worship of God has been compromised. So, for Jesus, the transformation of the tradition of the elders itself is a necessary outcome of radical trust in, and obedience to the living God of Israel. That is for him the way to life in lieu of those fruitless endeavors to gain divine acceptance and favor in the face of the threat of evil and condemnation.

It is also interesting to visualize Jesus speaking firmly, with certainty and authority, about the way of authentic spirituality right before he meets the woman in the borderlands and faces a seemingly different kind of conflict. Indeed, it may be argued that Jesus still needed to process more deeply, both existentially and theologically, the very meaning and implications of "tradition" being confronted by divine grace. Could it be that a difficult scanning process[6] requiring the collaboration of such a special stranger would eventually lead Jesus to further light, that is, a transformative learning that would translate into deeper caring and liberating power, and a clearer sense of vocation? With such a question in mind we now turn to that eventful encounter.

Focus on the encounter: Highlights of a stunning confrontation

A plain reading of the story presents a clear and unique instance in which Jesus yields. One could argue that here he is bested in an argument. The most striking and problematic part of the story is, of course, Jesus' initial response to the request of the woman: First a deafening silence, then an uncharacteristic affirmation of boundaries, followed by parabolic refusal. At that moment he appears to regard the woman's request as inappropriate, even as outrageously *out of place!* Only in this particular Gospel story does Jesus clearly ignore a supplicant, place the barrier of ethnicity before a plea for help, and then use offensive language to reiterate the barrier. Without question, "dog" is a disdainful metaphor, though Jesus uses a diminutive form ("puppy," "little bitch"). The implication, of course, is that the Gentiles/dogs have no place at the table. The woman, however, appears to play along with that harsh image and simply urges Jesus to take it one step further. She appeals to him as "Lord," asserts her

---

environment, selfhood, the possibilty of nonbeing [the Void], and the possibility of new being [the Holy]. All four dimensions are essential, and none of them can be ignored without decisive loss to our understanding of what is essentially human" (69).

[6] "Scanning" here denotes the conscious as well as unconscious process of seeking resolution to a given conflict situation, hopefully leading to new insight(s).

claim, and demonstrates her faith by arguing that at the very least both children (Jews) and dogs (Gentiles) are under the same caring, compassionate authority.

One need not infer that the woman agrees with the Gentile/dog analogy. Nor do we need to conclude that she considers herself unworthy and less than human, or that she identifies herself as a dog. On the contrary, we may assume that she is requesting that she and her daughter be included, that she hopes for a place at the table and challenges Israel's excluding ideology. When she says, "Yes, Lord ...," she agrees with Jesus that it would be wrong to throw the children's bread to the dogs. But she also reminds Jesus that if even dogs may eat what their masters waste, she and her daughter should receive bread, too. The Canaanite woman understands the grave meaning and the implications of Jesus' initial response, but she proceeds wisely and daringly to reframe and recast it. Jesus' original challenge to the woman merely restates the status quo of gender, ethnic, cultural, religious, and political divisions. Her counter-challenge calls him to look to the place of new possibilities across and beyond the established boundaries. Instead of accepting the dichotomy of children (insiders/receive food) versus dogs (outsiders/no food), she imagines that both the children and the dogs can be graciously fed inside, within the same household and from the same table.[7] Stated in other terms, the foreign woman is facing the "Void"[8] as she tries to deal with the painful reality of her daughter's torment, and begs for mercy. Jesus, however, initially appears to cling to the very two-dimensionality that he had earlier rejected. He seems to be pushed to face the possibility of his own faithlessness and abandonment of God at this point and, thereby, to come face to face with the holiness of God "beyond the boundaries" at the prompting of the foreign woman.

The dramatic import of this encounter in the borderlands is heightened as we recall its historical and textual background. "Show them no mercy," Moses had said to the people of Israel (Deut. 7:2). "Have mercy on me, Lord, Son of David," the Canaanite woman implores the New Moses of Israel. This Canaanite woman thus shatters the lingering image of wicked Canaanites, who presumably offer their children in sacrifice to their gods; she pleads on behalf of her daughter, who cannot speak for

---

[7] Elaine M. Wainwright lucidly argues this point in *Shall We Look for Another? A Feminist Rereading of the Matthean Jesus* (Maryknoll: Orbis Books, 1998), 86–92.

[8] In Loder's model, the Void ultimately denotes human existence "destined to annihilation ... irrevocable drift toward utter emptiness and nothingness which accompanies human existence from the time of birth [and] has many faces—such as loneliness, depression, and death." (*The Transforming Moment*), 230.

herself.[9] Well aware of his people's position and privilege as "chosen," Jesus initially reasserts the exclusiveness of his mission. But in the end, he welcomes the woman and she receives what she had sought with passion, courage, and determination.

Finally, this story parallels that of the Roman centurion in Mt 8:5–13. These are the only two healings in this Gospel explicitly involving Gentiles and accomplished from a distance. In both cases Jesus deems the people worthy of the gift of healing. In fascinating reversals, both Gentiles even become exemplar figures. Most commentators indicate that although Matthew's final word on mission to the Gentiles does not come until the last chapter of the Gospel (28:16–20), in these and related episodes the theme emerges that ethnicity does not define the people of God. Intertextual comparative studies indicate that Matthew's positive portrait of Jesus' response to the Gentiles constitutes a partial reversal of the Exodus tradition by focusing on the missional goal of bringing outsiders to the knowledge of the God of Israel.[10] God's purposes include Gentiles, and Jesus the Jew is the agent of divine grace on their behalf.[11] Transformation will happen in the borderlands.

The significance of the text: *Judging*

Above we raised the question whether Jesus, as a pastoral caregiver, needed to undergo a difficult "scanning" process requiring the collaboration of a foreign woman in the borderlands in order to further discern the nature and contours of divine grace. Earlier in the gospel text we saw him responding with clarity and certainty in the face of the challenge by Pharisees and scribes. Now he is treading unfamiliar territory

---

[9] For this way of restating the meaning of the encounter, I am indebted to my former student Leticia A. Guardiola-Sáenz, who shared with me a paper written during her doctoral work at Vanderbilt University (Summer 1998), "Jesus' Encounter with the Canaanite Woman: The 'Hybrid Moment' of the Matthean Community."

[10] Willard M. Swartley makes this point in *Israel's Scripture Traditions and the Synoptic Gospels: Story Shaping Story* (Peabody, Mass.: Hendrickson Pubs., Inc., 1994), 70.

[11] See, for instance, the fine commentary by Warren Carter, *Matthew and the Margins: A Sociopolitical and Religious Reading* (Maryknoll: Orbis Books, 2000), 320ff. Other recent biblical studies done with a "decolonizing" interest and perspective present a different picture as they attempt to unveil and deconstruct certain perceived biases in the biblical text. See, for example, Musa W. Dube, "A Postcolonial Feminist Reading of Matthew 15:21–28," pt. 3 of *Postcolonial Feminist Interpretation of the Bible* (St. Louis: Chalice Press, 2000). For this African scholar, "the divergent receptions accorded to the centurion and the Canaanite woman reflect the imperial and patriarchal currents at work in Matthew.... No doubt, the implied author, writing in the post-70 C.E. period, wishes to present the Matthean community as a nonsubversive community" (132–3). Dube's work includes serious critiques of the work of several white, western, middle-class feminist writers on this text (169–84). Her thesis and overall discussion are provocative; nevertheless, my

and the "context of rapport" of his circle of disciples does not seem to be particularly helpful.

The text before us suggests and calls for several kinds of stretching. Geographic, ethnic, gender, religious, theological, socio-cultural, moral, and political dimensions are involved. No wonder, then, that the intrusion of the woman into his life and sense of vocation and ministry stunned Jesus. Because this narrative has much spatial and contextual import, it is fitting that our interpretation underscores that this marginal Canaanite woman emerges as the center of the story! In fact, the story is primarily her story. We observe a surprising, transforming reversal: Jesus comes to acknowledge that she has *great* faith. This Gospel uses that adjective to describe faith only once. The woman's faith encompasses her persistent demand for inclusion in the face of Jesus' resistance; her challenge to the gender, ethnic, religious, political, and economic barriers; her recognition of Jesus' authority over demons; and her reliance on his power.[12] Perhaps Jesus' praise includes a realization we can appreciate today as well: In that encounter in the borderlands, the Canaanite woman became a prophetic and wise teacher. Out of her desire for healing for her daughter, she acted and spoke counter-culturally and counter-politically as she reminded Jesus of the larger vision of the reign of God. And she did so in a way consistent with the converging prophetic and wisdom traditions with which Jesus/ Wisdom (Sophia) is interpreted in the Gospel of Matthew.[13]

Put in other words, the Syrophoenician/Canaanite woman had approached Jesus as a care seeker on behalf of her daughter; in the process of her encounter with Jesus, she also ministered to him by eventually focusing on *negating (or contradicting) the negation* inherent in the dog-Gentile analogy traditionally used by the Jews. In terms of transformational logic, her bisociating insight indeed amounted to a constructive act of the imagination[14] which eventually resonated with Jesus' own imagination

---

appraisal is that she and other authors with similar perspectives often neglect to acknowledge inherent tensions and dialectical import within biblical texts, and thus fail to appreciate one key aspect of their liberating and transformative potential.

[12] Carter, *Matthew and the Margins*, 324–5.

[13] Wainwright, *Shall We Look for Another?*, 88.

[14] According to James Loder's own definitions, "bisociation" denotes the surprising convergence of two incompatible frames of reference to compose an original and meaningful unity; bisociation is the basic unit of an insight, which may include several bisociations to form a complex new meaning. And "constructive acts of imagination" are those insights, intuitions, or visions that appear— usually with convincing force—in the borderline area between consciousness and unconsciousness; they convey, in a form readily available to consciousness, the essence of a conflict resolution. Loder, *The Transforming Moment*, 222.

work. The encounter itself—the unique relationality linking Jesus and the foreign woman—was transformed: confrontation became a kind of collaborative work. And while the disciples seemed to fade to the background, the foreign woman became spiritually closer to Jesus.[15]

The most vexing question for us as pastoral caregivers and theologians is, of course, why Jesus would act as he initially did in this encounter. An answer requires that we maintain the tension between two historical realities pertaining to his socio-cultural experience or lived world. On the one hand, we must assume that Jesus had been socialized into the conventional wisdom of his time and dominant culture. According to such socialization, prudence involved keeping clear boundaries; adhering to certain criteria of what is proper, clean, normal, and appropriate; and holding to right categories and patterns of perception, thought, and relationships. This socialization was undoubtedly part of Jesus' identity as a first-century Jew. From a human science perspective, we do not expect that Jesus would have been exempt from dealing with prejudice. Neither do we expect that he would have spontaneously developed the kind of understanding enabling him to readily appreciate and communicate with the woman across vast ethnic, social, cultural, and religious differences. On the other hand, we must also recognize that Jesus of Nazareth was himself a marginal person.[16] He was rejected by the dominant groups and became a friend of marginalized people such as tax-collectors, outcasts, women, the poor and oppressed, "sinners," and Gentiles. In other words, Jesus related abnormally well to those people and was accepted by them, because he was himself an outsider, a homeless person (Mt 8:20) living in two worlds without fully belonging to either.[17] In sum, from a theological perspective, whenever we look at Jesus the Christ we should see that the historical and existential reality of the incarnation is not only about "body" (*sôma*), but is also about "soul" (*psyche*) and "spirit" (*pneuma*). In other words, we propose to take seriously the New Testament references

---

[15] A formal definition of when it is appropriate to identify change as *transformation*, is in order. According to Loder, "transformation occurs whenever, within a given frame of reference or experience, hidden orders of coherence and meaning emerge to replace or alter the axioms of the given frame and reorder its elements accordingly." *The Transforming Moment*, p. 229.

[16] For a scholarly treatment of the marginality of Jesus, see John P. Meier, A *Marginal Jew: Rethinking the Historical Jesus* (New York: Doubleday, 1991).

[17] Jung Young Lee has insightfully discussed the question of Jesus and marginality in *Marginality: The Key to a Multicultural Theology* (Minneapolis: Fortress Press, 1995). Writing from an Asian (Korean) American perspective, Lee proposes "a new theology based on marginality, which serves not only as a hermeneutical paradigm but as a key to the substance of the Christian faith" (1).

which point to a holistic anthropology.

An outsider, a multiply marginal person, challenged Jesus to relate and minister across and beyond those boundaries. She gave him an opportunity to respond in tune with God's alternative wisdom expressed in an ethic and politic of compassion and radical inclusiveness. It is fitting to conclude that Jesus faced a major conflict and temptation, indeed a temptation from within, and that eventually he chose wisely, even as he was creatively challenged by the foreign woman. This conclusion need not compromise the christological conviction about the nature and work of Jesus as Christ. As Hebrews 4:15 puts it, "We do not have a high priest who is unable to sympathize with our weaknesses, but we have one who in every respect has been tested as we are, yet without sin." If we accept this interpretation, we must reject three other interpretations: (a) that Jesus was testing (that is, playing games with) the woman while knowing all along what he should and would do; (b) that he wanted to teach the disciples a dramatic lesson about loving enemies; or, as proposed by some radical feminists, (c) that Jesus had to be converted (repent from sin). The biblical text supports none of these interpretations. On the contrary, it is our view that the text implies the triumph of Jesus' (and the foreign woman's) spirit grounded and sustained by the Spirit of God. In fact, in addition to pertinent christological consideration, this gospel story illumines the question of how the spiritual life can become transcendent and at the same time preserve its immanent integrity in the context of human experience.

As Jesus appropriated the woman's insight significantly expanding the contours of compassion and care, energy was released (he praised the woman in unusual terms, her daughter was healed, and then more miracles took place), and Jesus further engaged in interpretation and ministry in the light of God's reign. The personal drama and the behavior of the Syrophoenician/Canaanite woman became a kind of catalyst of the multifaceted transforming encounter in the borderlands: many barriers were broken, temptation was overcome, understandings were deepened, faith was affirmed, and a child was healed.

The story as it unfolds makes clear that both the woman and Jesus became boundary walkers and boundary breakers. By eventually choosing to relate and to minister "out of place," Jesus and the woman pointed the way to God's utopia. "Utopia" means literally "no place," not in the sense of never-never land, illusion, or fantasy, but as the stuff of prophetic dreams. From a biblical perspective, utopias are places that are not yet, not because they are mere ideals beyond reach, but because evil and sinful structures and behaviors resist and contradict God's will for multidimensional (that is, ethnic, social, cultural, and religious) justice and reconciliation.

Finally, as we judge this text, we must realize its significance in light of the social and existential realities of the Matthean community. On the one hand, we recognize that the Gospel according to Matthew was written from the perspective of the chosen people of Israel, beginning with "Jesus the Messiah, the son of David, the son of Abraham" (Matt. 1:1). The author writes from the center of the tradition, and from a typically "centralist" point of view.[18] Within this framework Jesus instructs the disciples, "Go nowhere among the Gentiles …, but go rather to the lost sheep of the house of Israel" (Matt. 10:5–6). The latter expression is unique to Matthew and repeated in our text. The author leaves no doubt about Israel's priority in salvation history. On the other hand, the story of the Canaanite woman can help undermine and even dismantle—that is, dialectically speaking, negate the negation imposed by—chosenness as ideology, as justification for excluding and discriminating against the other, the stranger, the foreigner, the "pagan." A powerful paradox is at work here!

We surmise that the early readers of Matthew were Jewish Christians separated from the synagogue and relating both to a largely Gentile Christian movement and to the Jewish community. The story must have aided them to understand their new place and role in God's plan and reign. This story may also have helped free them from the ideology of chosenness so they could be transformed into a more liberating and inclusive faith community. Perhaps they were already beginning to experience such a community, but were unsure about how to cope with, legitimate, and reflect on it.[19] This transition and transformation of the Matthean community would have been crucial for their sense of identity as well as for the mission to the Gentiles. The new community—where there is no longer Jew or Greek, slave or free, male and female, for all are one in Christ (Gal. 3:28)—is thus called to celebrate, embody, and be an agent of the coming reign of God, the future in which God is making all things new. Transformation would indeed happen in the borderlands!

Embodying the text: *Acting*

In this final section we must focus on application. We will do that in

---

[18] Lee, *Marginality*, 116.

[19] See Leticia A. Guardiola-Sáenz's helpful discussion of this question in "Borderless Women and Borderless Texts: A Cultural Reading of Matthew 15:21–28," *Semeia* 78 (1997): 69–81.

light of the two questions presented at the beginning of this study: how may this biblical text become foundational for caregiving ministry? How may this unique story further illumine the challenges and possibilities of intercultural and interfaith spiritual care for Christian caregivers?

We may realize the creative and liberating potential of this story in many ways on personal and communal levels. The following interrelated guidelines illustrate how this text has become foundational for me and other pastoral caregivers or, in other words, how the text has ministered to us so that we can minister to others in intercultural and interfaith situations. Without trivializing the import of this wonderful story, I will briefly discuss three ways our text foundationally illumines specific and interrelated principles—that is, dependable guides to practice—for caregiving ministry.

Marginality, vulnerability, and *vision*

First, contrary to what dominant cultures hold, the borderlands can become privileged places for the blessings of creative and transformative caring and for personal and communal growth and healing. Conventional and pragmatic wisdom favors the safe havens of familiar territory, the shrewd and sensible stance of "playing it safe." The story of the Canaanite woman who confronts Jesus helps us realize that we can see reality better at places of marginality and vulnerability and from the vantage point available to us at the borders. Our vision may thus be transformed. Hence, we are called to creative "willful contextual dislocations."[20] This story asks us to move deliberately beyond our comfort zones, either by going out or by welcoming into our midst the stranger, the alien, or the different other. By moving from the center to the margins, we will find our perspectives significantly changed: we will become aware of the lenses through which we view the world, and our cultural and ideological captivities will be unveiled. We will be open to see better how God wants us to live and care for others in creative, redeeming, and empowering ways wherever we are.

Interfaith spiritual care situations present unique challenges and opportunities for pastoral caregivers to grow in *vision*, in the sense of perceiving care seekers and the very relationship of care with the eyes

---

[20] I have described the notion of willful (or voluntary) dislocation in connection with transformative learning in Daniel S. Schipani, "Liberation Theology and Religious Education," in *Theologies of Religious Education*, ed. Randolph Crump Miller (Birmingham: Religious Education Press, Inc., 1995), 308–10; and "Educating for Social Transformation," in *Mapping Christian Education: Approaches to Congregational Learning*, ed. Jack L. Seymour (Nashville: Abingdon Press, 1997), 37–8.

of God, as it were. That growth includes a number of dimensions and practices such as these: attentiveness, contemplation, and respectful and appreciative awareness of the uniqueness and value of the care receiver; critical thinking and creative imagination to deal with and transform barriers to communication and understanding and collaboration; spiritual discernment: (a) to recognize the care receivers' actual needs, hopes, and resourcefulness in their own terms; (b) to make available specific, pertinent care; and (c) to be intentionally open to receiving the spiritual gifts provided by those of other faiths. Finally, growth in *vision*, thus understood, must be considered together with growth in *virtue* and *vocation*, as defined below.

Conflict, suffering, and *virtue*

A second guideline suggested by our study is that situations of conflict and suffering can become opportunities for transformation, for renewal and healing, and for witnessing God's amazing grace. People who hunger and thirst for wholeness, justice, freedom, and peace are especially close to the heart of God because their desire reflects God's own longing for all people. For this reason they are blessed (Mt 5:3–11). For this reason the Canaanite woman was blessed. That is the meaning of the claim of liberation theologies, that God has a preferential option for the poor and oppressed, for the victim and the weak. According to the four Gospels, Jesus not only taught about this preference, he also showed concretely what it involves. In our story, the demonstration happened in a context of conflict and against Jesus' human inclinations! Christian pastoral caregivers are sent to continue his ministry and to embrace the ailing and suffering neighbor who longs for healing and hope. As we respond, our hearts will be nurtured and transformed.

Interfaith spiritual caregiving thus presents unique challenges and opportunities for pastoral caregivers to grow in *virtue*, in the sense of their hearts being formed in the light of Jesus Christ. In other words, the notion of "virtue" (singular) in this essay denotes the moral character of the caregiver. It can be described in terms of our innermost dispositions and attitudes, that is, the "habits of the heart" which help define the content of "Christian character." These are the deep affections and passions and, especially, the kinds of virtues (plural)[21] that, at their best,

---

[21] "Virtues" (in the plural) are those specific moral strengths, skills or capacities, and habits, which have particular moral significance. They are values that become character shaped by practice and discipline. Virtues are thus personal qualities constitutive of the moral character of pastoral caregivers, hopefully reflective of the character of the very faith communities they represent.

faith communities seek to foster and form in their members as genuine expressions of divine love and a way of life in the power of the Spirit. For pastoral caregivers, therefore, interfaith situations may become special places of grace as we are led and empowered to practice the values and the virtues essential for caring as representatives of Christ, such as humility, hospitality, love, compassion, patience, hope, generosity, and courage.

Mutuality, mission, and *vocation*

Third, as Jesus himself may have experienced, ministry at its best is a two-way street, a mutual practice and process. For us in North America, the center of the center in the ongoing globalization process, this kind of ministry poses special challenges. To become truly "missional," our faith communities will have to undergo a conversion to the margins. Many of us Christians need to shed our exclusivist ideology of chosenness to better attend to our deepest yearnings, limitations, and needs, as well as to the potential and resourcefulness of others. We bless and we are in turn blessed, sometimes the hard way, in spite of our blinders and shortcomings. Often we will unexpectedly find ourselves being ministered to. In fact, we cannot truly participate in other people's liberation and healing without allowing them to participate in our own liberation and healing.

Interfaith spiritual caregiving presents unique challenges and opportunities for pastoral caregivers to grow in *vocation*, in the sense of partnership with the Spirit as the essence of our ministerial practice. In the process of interfaith caregiving our common human vocation in the light of God can be reconfirmed and sustained. Furthermore, for us today the twofold blessing of mutuality and partnership may include an additional realization: caring and being cared for in the borderlands, across and against boundaries of culture and faith, again and again becomes the sacred experience of encountering and loving Christ anew. In due time it will be revealed to us, as in the eschatological parable of Mt 25:31–46:[22] "Truly I tell you, just as you did it to one of the least of these who are members of my family, you did it to me."

---

[22] Matthew's judgment scene in 25:31–46 is the culmination of a two-chapter eschatological discourse, and it has been interpreted in diverse ways. In any event, two things should be kept in mind. First, for Matthew, Jesus is identified with the (marginalized) community of disciples, and he is present with them as they engage in mission to communicate the gospel (18:20, 28:20). Second, in this text Jesus praises the actions of the righteous from "all the nations" (presumably Gentiles as well as Jews and Christians) because they have lived out the gospel by caring for the poor, oppressed, and marginalized; the actions of these "sheep" blessed by the Father are the practices of service expected of gospel bearers, followers of Jesus Christ.

Appendix

On the wideness of compassion in the witness of Scripture

An interpretive survey of Old and New Testament material allows us to highlight scriptural sources for an affirmation of the boundless reach of Grace in the face of diversity, including multifaith settings. In the words of W. Eugene March: "[We are] well aware and appreciative of an explicit narrative in the Bible that focuses first on God's people, Israel, and then widens to include Christians and the church. The election of each of these peoples for specific service to God and on God's behalf in the world is clear. But there is another, implicit narrative … this has to do with God's ongoing relationship with others beyond Israel and the church. The service entrusted to Israel and the church assumes that all people are creatures of God and the objects of divine love."[23] Those biblical sources may, therefore, help us to undergird caregiving ministry in interfaith situations. What follows is a selection of such foundational material in summary fashion.[24]

Old Testament background

- Genesis 1:26–27. All humans are created as spiritual beings "in [God's] image," "according to [God's] likeness."

- Genesis 3. All humans share the predicament of struggle and potential alienation resulting in the need for manifold care.

- Genesis 9:1–17. God's covenant with Noah is an all-inclusive, fundamental, and universal "covenant of life," which is not cancelled by other covenants recorded in Scripture.

- Genesis 11:1–9. The story of the tower of Babel symbolizes the human will to concentrate and consolidate and the tendency towards power and domination. It represents disobedience to the divine mandate to "scatter and fill the earth"— which indicates that it is diversity, rather than homogeneity or uniformity, that is the outgrowth of God's design for human culture.

- Genesis 12:3. Those who claim to be the chosen people of God

---

[23] W. Eugene March, *The Wide, Wide Circle of Divine Love: A Biblical Case for Religious Diversity* (Louisville: Westminster John Knox, 2004), x.

[24] See also, Cynthia M. Campbell, *A Multitude of Blessings: A Christian Approach to Religious Diversity* (Lousville: Westminster John Knox, 2007). In this book the author makes a compelling case: it is possible, indeed necessary, to paradoxically embrace the reality and value of religious diversity in terms of God's providential care for all of humankind, while also affirming the Christian confession that God has made Godself uniquely known to humankind in the life, death, and resurrection of Jesus.

are called to become a blessing "to all families," "to the nations." This is the key to the human vocation of partnership with Grace, which may be uniquely enacted in pastoral care ministry.

- Leviticus 19:24, Deuteronomy 10:17. "You shall love the alien as yourself … the Lord … loves the strangers." Welcoming and caring for the stranger: interfaith spiritual care can and must be a special case of hospitable compassion.

- Subversive stories (in addition to the role of "religious others"— Hagar, Asenath, Zipporah, Cyrus, and many others): Ruth the Moabite, the foreigner pagan becomes "one of us" and much more. Jonah, reluctant "missionary," reveals nagging divine compassion for the sake of strangers "lost."

- Wisdom books—Job, Proverbs, Ecclesiastes, parts of Psalms— and wisdom theology as a form of practical theology: they focus on human experience and predicament and draw from many wellsprings (including extra-biblical sources) for discernment of truthful knowledge and the way of the good life.

- Jeremiah 18:18. The gifts of priests/instruction, prophets/word, and sages/counsel summarize the biblical canon as well as the main "offices" for the formation and transformation of Israel as people of God. Those very gifts may be applied and bestowed especially in interfaith care situations.

New Testament guidelines

- John 1:14, 20:21. The key to an incarnation theology and ministry of presence: the Word (Logos=Wisdom) became flesh and lived among us. Pastoral caregivers may view themselves as sent by Jesus to embody good news (John 20:21).

- Story meets story: the narrative shape of the gospel encounters the narrative quality of human experience: the Jesus story and the stories Jesus told in light of our stories. Pastoral caregivers may view themselves as bearers of the Story, witnesses to the unfolding drama of care receivers' life stories, and mediators between and among stories.

- Luke 4:16–27. "The Spirit of the Lord is upon me …" Pastoral caregivers committed to minister in the manner and with the spirit of Jesus may become radically inclusive instruments of liberation and healing empowered by the same Spirit.

- Mark 4:3–8. Parable of the sower: sent to sow generously and joyfully. Pastoral caregivers do not calculate beforehand if/how/when/where the seed will fall on "good soil" but go about the task with liberal, gracious freedom; they know that making things grow is not their concern because growth [formation and transformation] is in the hands of Another; they trust that, at the end of the day, there will be a surprisingly abundant harvest!

- Matthew 13:24–30. The parable of the wheat and the weeds. Suspend discrimination and judgment: Pastoral caregivers involved in interfaith situations must not dismiss, disregard, undervalue, the seemingly undeserving care receivers; they must care for everybody with equal diligence, competence, and generosity, regardless of religious affiliation, faith tradition, or type of spirituality; they must refrain from condemnation while trusting divine wisdom, mercy, and justice.

- Matthew 25:31–46. The parable of the judgment of the nations: Seeing and serving Jesus in interfaith situations. Pastoral caregivers may recognize and honor their daily walk into/within sacred places because visiting the sick strangers and their relatives (other-than-Christian) is an occasion to care for "one of the least of these …"; instead of trying to "bring Jesus" to the care receivers, they can confidently expect to encounter Christ in them and to care for Christ, as it were, through them: ("When did we see you …? I was a stranger and you welcomed me … I was sick and you took care of me."); they allow those strangers—"the least of these"—to become a blessing in turn.

- Luke. 10:25–37. Unexpected sources of revelation—encountering the (good) Samaritans: Pastoral caregivers engaged in interfaith situations may discover new dimensions of meaning and love through caring especially well for those who are different or a "minority"; re-discover gospel truth by being open to the faith of another (e.g. the gratitude of the Samaritan leper who was healed [Luke 17:16]); experience conversion again and again (becoming the Christian caregiver who looks more like the good Samaritan, the good Jew, Muslim, Hindu, Humanist…).

- John 4:1–41. Jesus and the Samaritan woman—interfaith encounters involve different kinds of dynamics. Pastoral caregivers may become aware of, and able to deal with, cross-cultural and interreligious realities, and gender dynamics; willing to become vulnerable for the sake of care; and able to assess care receivers' spiritual needs as well as their resourcefulness.

- Mark 7:24–30. Jesus and the Syrophoenician or Cannanite woman: the risks, challenges and blessings of ministering at the margins. Wise pastoral caregivers ministering in the borderlands of interfaith situations will discover that: places of marginality, ambiguity, or paradox may become places of grace; tension and conflict connected with socio-cultural and spiritual-theological factors (e.g. temptation not to minister) can turn into occasions for new insight and other learnings, emotional and spiritual growth; and ministry, at its best, is always a two-way street.

- Luke 7, Acts 10. Other "outsiders" cared for: the possibility of recognizing the presence, goodness, and power of God is not limited to the "people of God," because "God shows no partiality..." Christian pastoral caregivers may become mediators of grace and not only recognize and affirm the spirituality of people of other faiths but delight in the interface of spiritual paths involving care seekers and caregivers.

- Acts 2:1–13. From confusion and alienation to communication and communion: Pentecost and the reversal of Babel (Genesis 11:1–9), without destroying diversity. Pastoral caregivers may partner with the Spirit as they become spiritually and theologically "multilingual," develop the skills of translating Good News through a variety of languages and cultural frameworks, and wisely practice spiritual assessment and specific caregiving work with discernment.

A Lutheran chaplain's nine theses on interfaith care ministry

John D. Peterson

One spring afternoon in 1971, I was sitting in the downstairs hallway of True Light Lutheran Church in New York City's Chinatown, when a Buddhist monk in saffron robes and sandals walked into the Missouri Synod church. The monk spoke in Chinese to the several young members of the church to whom I had been talking. "He wants a drink of water," one of the teenagers told me as another went to get a glass of water. His thirst satisfied, the monk went on his way. What makes this experience over 30 years ago memorable to me is the sense of anxiety and threat I felt as this very different man of a very different god entered what I considered to be Lutheran territory, and my relief when he left. The young folks thought it was neat and remarkable that they had had the opportunity to show kindness and care to a worthy stranger with a need that was easily satisfied. But to me, the Vicar [seminary intern], two very different theological planets had nearly collided.

Almost thirty years of hospital ministry have caused my working theology to become deeper and broader. While traditional Lutheran theology takes a polemic stance toward other religions, insights central to Reformation theology are helpful for spiritual caregivers in relation to those of other faiths. I found many references in Luther's writings about Jewish or Muslim people; all have been polemic, and not understanding or compassionate in tone. However, I chalk this up to the context in those pre-Renaissance times—strikingly different than the present day in terms of the amount of diversity and pluralism expected and tolerated in the world.

Coming into hospital ministry, I learned from the outset that the role of chaplain precludes an apologetic or competitive stance toward patients

John D. Peterson, D.Min., is a supervisor of Clinical Pastoral Education and Director of the Pastoral Care Division at Lutheran Hospital of Indiana, Fort Wayne, Indiana.

who present other (religious and non-religious) faiths. Patients and family members are in a dependent, 'one-down' position, and chaplains who used their access to patients to proselytize would be taking advantage of the patient's extreme vulnerability. There is a place for explicitly witnessing to one's faith or convictions, but it is when care seekers have control of their own environment, and can respond or engage with freedom and integrity.

Conversely, Christian chaplains have a rare opportunity to convey the power of the very grace that is the cornerstone of the Christian faith when they minister to the patient with respect and awareness of the patient's own belief system. In the movie, *The Shoes of the Fisherman*,[1] Russian Cardinal Kiril Lakota, newly made pope, escapes the confines of the Vatican and walks the streets, taking in the sounds and smells of Rome at dinnertime. A doctor approaches and asks him to hurry, fill a prescription. Father Kiril returns and enters the house. The family is Jewish and is shocked to see a priest, especially when he tries to give the dying man Last Rites. When a family member announces their Jewish faith, they respond with wonder and joy as Kiril begins to chant Kaddish. A similar joy is often evident when Christian chaplains are able to reach across religious boundaries and minister to patients on the care receivers' own terms.

Caring for Ahmet: A case study

The case study that follows is typical for interfaith pastoral visits that occur in the mid-western setting of the hospital in which I serve. The hospital itself was begun over 100 years ago by Lutherans, seeking to realize their understanding of Jesus' directive to care for the sick and injured. I direct a Clinical Pastoral Education (CPE) program within this hospital, and many of the visits made in our hospital are made by students. There are relatively few organized faith communities in the area that are not Christian, but, with increased immigration, there are now Muslim, Buddhist, Hindu as well as the more established Jewish communities in the area.

Preliminary data

The patient, whom I will call Ahmet, is of East European origin, aged 39, married. He is hospitalized with heart and kidney problems. Ahmet is an electrician and the visit is a random one, made one afternoon as the student chaplain was making rounds on his assigned unit.

---

[1] The film, *The Shoes of the Fisherman*, was directed by Michael Anderson and produced by Metro-Goldwyn-Mayer, in 1968.

The Chaplain, whom I will call Douglas, is an ordained minister in an independent evangelical church. He is in part-time CPE and is also an assistant minister in an area congregation. He had had a difficult morning at the church and internally resisted coming to the hospital to make visits. "I asked God to prepare my heart for what I would encounter that afternoon." Douglas is learning to be more alert to the non-verbal communication that goes on in pastoral conversations, and especially strives to be alert to "the patient's attitudes as we talk and if there is anything that is especially bothering them." He also tries "to be a spiritual and emotional encourager to the person I am visiting," and to be sure that he doesn't allow "my 'emotional baggage' to get in the way of my ministry."

The Situation: The patient was sitting up on the side of the bed. He appeared to be a little fidgety. The television was on. Ahmet was a very polite gentleman who spoke with an accent. He appeared receptive to Douglas's visit and was willing to talk.

Content of verbatim

C = Chaplain
P = Patient

C1 (Chaplain knocks) Good afternoon, my name is Douglas and I am one of the chaplains here at the hospital. May I come in and visit with you for a few minutes?

P1 Sure come on in, I would love some company. (He spoke with an accent that I could not recognize at first).

C2 How do you pronounce your first name—Ahmet?

P2 That is correct. And you pronounce your first name—Douglas?

C3 That is correct, (laughter). I won't even try to pronounce your last name, but I am sure that I would mispronounce it.

P3 Oh it is easy. It is pronounced_____. See how simple that is! (He laughs, knowing that it is a hard name to pronounce).

C4 How long have you been here in the hospital?

P4 I have been here about a week, but I hope that I will get to go home tomorrow. Even so, I know that I am going to have to come back for some surgery at some time.

C5 What kind of surgery are you going to need to have?

P5 Well, I came into the hospital because I was having heart problems and while I was here they found I had kidney problems and now I am on dialysis. Sometime I am going to need a kidney transplant, but first they have to find a suitable donor for me.

C6 Is there someone in your family who is a good match, like a brother or sister?

P6 No, so far they have not been able to locate anyone, but perhaps I have some family in Europe who would make for a good match.

C7 What part of Europe are you originally from? I could not identify your accent.

P7 I am originally from Bosnia and I lived there until ten years ago when I came to the United States. I still have family back in Bosnia.

C8 What was it like living in Bosnia? All I really know about Bosnia is what I have seen on TV or have read in the newspaper.

P8 Bosnia was a very hard place to live with all of the fighting. I served in the Bosnian army for a number of years. It is very hard watching your friends being shot and killed. I was one of the lucky ones to get out alive. War is terrible and it benefits no one. All of the fighting is especially hard on the young who are left homeless and who have one or both of their parents killed in the fighting. It is also very hard on the old people of our land who are left with nothing.

C9 I have never been in the military or been involved in a war, so I can only imagine what it must have been like for you. You are right when you say that war benefits no one, and everyone pays a price of some kind for the fighting.

P9 I hope that you never have to go to war or serve in the army. Do you have children?

C10 Yes, my wife and I have two sons who are 23 and 26 years old.

P10 I hope that your sons never have to go to war either, or have to be in the army.

C11 What brought you to the United States?

P11 I have an older brother who was already living here and he was an electrician. I came to work with him and to help him start his own business. I did not know much about electricity when I came, but he has taught me much about what being an electrician means. So now I work on other people's wiring and I am here in the hospital because I need to have some of my own wiring worked on. That is a poor joke isn't it?

C12 At least you have been able to keep some sense of humor and laughter in the situation. Laughter is sometimes a good medicine for us when we are hurting and struggling with the problems of life. Another help during our times of struggle is our faith. Do you have any type of religious faith to lean on during this time?

P12 My religious background is Muslim. Do you know anything about the Muslim faith?

C13 I know a little bit about the Muslim faith, but I also know that there is more that I do not know. I do know that the Muslim faith and the Christian faith have the same roots originally in the person of Abraham.

P13 Tell me chaplain, why do we have so many different religions in the world and how did they come about?

C14 Wow, that is a big question. I suppose that I could try to give a short answer. We have so many different religions because we have so many different kinds of people with different religious viewpoints. Originally there was just one religion, the worship of Yahweh God, but then somebody had a different idea and a new religion grew up. And we see that same scenario happening down through the ages, until today we have hundreds of different religions.

[Douglas's opinion here is, of course, offered extemporaneously and is certainly incorrect in that there were a variety of religions in the world already in the time of Abraham.]

P14 That is kind of the way it was with Christianity and the Muslim faith.

C15 Yes, we all come from the same source. Abraham who is the father of the Hebrew nation believed in Yahweh God and he had two sons: Isaac and Ishmael. From the line of Isaac the Hebrew faith came about and from Ishmael came the Muslim faith.

P15 In the Muslim faith we believe in Jesus, but only as a good prophet, where you believe in him as the Son of God. We believe in a lot of the prophets and their teachings. A lot of what is written in the Koran is also written in your Bible. I think that we believe in the same God, but we use different names to describe Him. What bothers me is that there are so many Muslims who use their religion for other purposes, they do not even follow what the Koran is really saying, they change it to fit what they want to do. It bothers me when some Muslims use their faith as an excuse for killing other people simply to get what they want. The Koran does not teach us to do that. That is wrong. That is not religion.

C16 You know, Ahmet, people have been doing that same thing for years. Look back in history at the time of the Crusades and the Holy

Wars that were fought, all under the heading of religion. I think we will always have people who will use their religion as a means to accomplish what they want and who give no thought to what God really wants. It makes it harder to argue against someone's actions if they justify them for religious reasons.

P16 You are very right.

C17 Listen to us—we sound like a couple of philosophers who are trying to figure out how we can change the world and solve all the problems of the world. (We both laugh). I have enjoyed our conversation—it has been very stimulating. I sure do hope that they can find a match for you for a kidney replacement. If there is anything that I can do for you while you are here, please feel free to have one of the nurses page me, and if I am not here, one of our other chaplains will be happy to help you. Before I take my leave, may I pray for you in the name of Yahweh our God?

P17 I would appreciate that.

C18 Dear God, I want to thank you for this day and the blessings that you have provided for both Ahmet and me. I want to thank you that two people from different parts of the world could sit down and talk about life and religion the way we have this afternoon. I thank you for the opportunity to meet Ahmet and to hear a portion of his story. Dear God I want to thank you for the things that we have in common and the opportunity that we have had to be able to encourage each other this afternoon. I want to also pray that you would be with Ahmet as he prepares to go home in the next couple of days, that the problems with his heart have been corrected. And I also pray that you would be with him in the weeks ahead, that a suitable kidney donor might be found. I pray your care and your blessing might be upon him. These things I pray in the name of Yahweh, the God of Abraham and our God. Amen.

P18 Amen. Thank you Douglas for visiting me and praying with me.

C19 It was a privilege Ahmet. The best of luck to you.

Pastoral and spiritual assessment

Early in the visit, Chaplain Douglas was aware that he was visiting someone with a very different set of beliefs. The patient's welcoming attitude and openness facilitated the visit. Douglas tried to be respectful of the patient's belief system, which was made difficult by his awareness that he actually knew little about the patient's faith system. "I tried to find areas where we had common ground and to build off of those areas." Chaplain

Douglas felt good that the dialogue included principles that he considers Christian, such as respect for persons despite differences, and demonstration of compassion for fellow humans.

Chaplain Douglas wished he had explored the call of Abram a little more in Genesis 12 and how that call related to each of them. "The story of Abraham is … a faith story of a man who knew the value of trusting in God, a concept that we could have developed more fully.

Chaplain Douglas assessed the relationship he developed with Ahmet as meaningful in that they both learned something new about each other and about their religious faiths. He appreciated both Ahmet's commitment to his faith system, as well as his disappointment with those who misuse that faith system for their own agendas. Douglas appreciated Ahmet's openness and the questions he asked, even though they moved the discussion away from Ahmet's hospitalization and immediate situation, to a more global discussion.

Nevertheless, Douglas saw the trust implicit in the patient's broad questions. I was uncertain whether Ahmet was eagerly taking advantage of an opportunity for a heartfelt discussion that would explore his faith with the chaplain for whom he felt some initial trust, and who represented the dominant religious paradigm of his adopted culture, or whether his questions represented a theological distraction that would keep the discussion global, and safely away from the intimacy of an existential discussion about his hospitalization.[2] My training and experience as a CPE supervisor leaves me with a bias toward the latter interpretation, that of an ambivalent patient and a student chaplain, colluding to avoid intimacy. Perhaps it was both!

Douglas was not aware of any desire to change Ahmet's belief system: "I felt like we were two sons of Abraham who were able to come together on some common ground. I believe that I was able to minister to him, and he certainly ministered to me."

Chaplain Douglas saw his role as that of emotional and spiritual "encourager" for this patient. He felt he was able to do this to the extent that they were able to establish "some common ground to work from." Douglas also thought that his presence and conversation were forces of encouragement for the patient. "Jesus taught us that we are to love one another and I believe that we were both able to demonstrate that principle in how we dialogued." Douglas saw the patient's permission for prayer as evidence that some trust had been established.

---

[2] Similar to the sense I make of the comment in another interfaith discussion, that of the woman at Jacob's well in her encounter with Jesus. John 4:19–20.

Chaplain Douglas presented this verbatim with the following questions: (1) He was unsure if he should have (or could have?) gone further in discussing the divergent views of Jesus that surfaced in the dialogue. (2) He wanted feedback on his sensitivity "to the extreme difference in our faith systems." (3) Douglas wanted feedback on his attempts to balance his attention to the patient's physical needs, emotional needs and spiritual needs.

Summary of group and supervisory feedback

The supervisor realized that this was a first experience of ministry to a person of another faith system by this relative newcomer to hospital ministry. Douglas comes from a conservative, evangelical background, theologically, and his attempt to honor the inclusive approach to ministry that is part of CPE orientation in our hospital was evident.

The feedback given to Douglas was similar to his own ministry approach in that we tried to be encouraging—encouraging of his attempt to find common ground in his spiritual discussion with Ahmet, and his willingness to find ways to fully accept this man for being a fellow human. It was suggested to Douglas that he could have focused more attention on listening to the patient, for example, in the religious part of the discussion, asking Ahmet to teach him about the Muslim faith, especially those parts that were helpful in times of sickness and uncertainty. The group also encouraged Douglas to use the experience to find out more about ways of ministering to Muslims. There was doubt expressed about the "prayer to Yahweh" (the Hebrew name for "LORD") as being an appropriate way to minister to a Muslim. Finally, a seminar was scheduled for the group, featuring a hospital physician who is a practicing Muslim. My own curiosity was awakened by this visit about our widespread inclination to find "common ground" when confronted by a difference. Are there other, better ways to proceed?

Interfaith pastoral care and Lutheranism

When Luther posted 95 theses on the Castle Church door in the university town of Wittenburg in Germany 490 years ago, he was seeking to promote a theological discussion about the practice of indulgences. In a similar way, I would like to offer the following nine theses regarding ways in which Lutheran theology offers perspective on pastoral care to those of other faith traditions. My perspective draws on my experience as chaplain and supervisor of Clinical Pastoral Education in historically Lutheran institutions, as well as eight years in parish ministry.

Lutheran theology lifts up the importance of the individual

Martin Luther was at the forefront of leaders in both church and society of his day who gave new value to the interior and exterior human life. The human conscience and the individual human's behavior and goals suddenly became important. The Christian chaplain who ministers to persons of another faith can carry the value that 'every person's life is worth a novel,' that every person's experience, sense of right and wrong, is valuable.

The Christian caregiver is freed from anxiety of the law

Luther's own faith journey was initially fueled by a search for relief from anxiety; in his case, anxiety about a God whom he experienced as enraged about human sin. He constantly worried that his own actions and thoughts were not good enough, and acts of painful and damaging self-mortification in order to appease this wrathful God were of only temporary help.[3] In his great awakening, Luther discovered that the Gospel meant that Christ's merit interceded so that believers were set free from terror about God's righteous wrath. They were forgiven, for Christ's sake, freed from anxiety and freed to love and to serve. I draw great comfort from the Gospel as I minister to those of other faiths. I am set free from the anxiety that I feel in the presence of a different theological world. The Gospel means that I can be a non-anxious presence, reflecting, as best I can, God's love to fellow humans.

The Christian is called to live in trust that God's love is for the whole world

The eminent Swedish Lutheran theologian, Krister Stendahl, once stated that "God's agenda is the mending of creation."[4] Even though individuals are important to God, it is important for Christian caregivers to see the larger picture. Luther stressed that God's love is for all humans, and that humans are called to love neighbors whether they were seen as friend or foe.

Convinced of God's enduring love, the Christian is called into vocation

Some of Luther's most valuable insights have to do with his theology of vocation. To Luther, butchers, bakers, and candlestick makers have been called by God and have vocations that are just as valid as those held by pastors and teachers. All work to provide sustenance to humans and to a world with many levels of needs. God chooses to accomplish many

---

[3] For a very readable and accurate study of Luther's life, including *Anfechtungen* [spiritual struggles] see Roland Bainton, *Here I Stand: A Life of Martin Luther*, Abington-Cokesbury, 1950.

[4] Krister Stendahl, as quoted by Roland E. Miller, "Christ the Healer," in Henry L. Lettermann, ed., *Health and Healing: Ministry of the Church*, (Chicago: Wheat Ridge Foundation Symposium Papers, 1980), 16.

purposes on earth by calling humans to the ongoing job of care. In the hospital setting, this idea of vocation has been helpful in seeing nurses and physicians regardless of their faith traditions, as well as chaplains, as ministers.

Ministry to persons of other faiths needs to be more than just "evangelism"

No matter the Christian's specific vocation, the basic job description is to love our neighbor. As we are involved in service and ministry, addressing human needs, we are involved in what can be called the *penultimate*.[5] We feed the hungry, provide shelter for the homeless, encourage those who are sick and injured. As we do so, we trust that God is working through us, addressing the *ultimate* concerns. Luther was motivated to speak out about indulgences because he saw that the entire approach of the church toward individuals had been relegated to travelling salesmen. In our day and society it is sometimes a danger that we develop a similar tunnel vision, reducing 'outreach' to the point that it becomes synonymous with a kind of evangelism that is divorced from care and listening. When this happens the valid ministry of evangelism is reduced to a sales pitch, and the gospel is reduced to a 'product.' Our unavoidable and irreducible vocation is to love our neighbors, trusting that God will call whom God will call.

Pastoral care to those of other faiths is not extraneous, but central to the church's mission

A remarkable letter has recently been sent from an international group of eminent Muslim scholars to Jewish and Christian religious leaders.[6] The letter calls for solidarity and common advocacy for peace and witness to the world, an invitation to base this collaboration in the faiths' agreement that believers are called to love God and to love the neighbor. This God-ordained hospitality is at its fullest when we are welcoming the stranger,

---

[5] Dietrich Bonhoeffer, *Ethics* (New York: MacMillan, 1955), 82. Cited in Edward E. Thornton, *Theology and Pastoral Counseling* (Englewood Cliffs: Prentice-Hall, Inc., 1964), 39: "No one has the last word, yet everyone may have the next-to-last word."

[6] "A Common Word Between Us and You." See the official website: http://www.acommonword. com: On October 13, 2006, one month to the day after Pope Benedict XVI's Regensburg address of September 13, 2006, 38 Islamic authorities and scholars from around the world, representing all denominations and schools of thought, joined together to deliver an answer to the Pope in the spirit of open intellectual exchange and mutual understanding. In their *Open Letter to the Pope*, for the first time in recent history, Muslim scholars from every branch of Islam spoke with one voice about the true teachings of Islam. Now, exactly one year after that letter, Muslims have expanded their message. In *A Common Word Between Us and You*, 138 Muslim scholars, clerics and intellectuals have unanimously come together for the first time since the days of the Prophet to declare the common ground between Christianity and Islam.

when we show love to those who have been seen as enemy.

The Christian is always *simul iustus et peccator* (simultaneously just and sinner)

This phrase was used by Luther to describe a paradox of the Christian life: we are saints, trying to make God the center of our being, yet our vision always curves in on itself.[7] Our God is always too small, because we fashion our perceptions of the Divine in our own image and marginalize those whose image is different. Luther thought that it was always dangerous to anthropomorphize God. This, in a subtle way, puts us at center stage. If God is just like us, it's only reasonable to make others be like us as well. Luther had a healthy skepticism about councils and synods and the decisions they make. The Church always needs reforming. I experience myself as being called to care for those of other faiths, not because my God is small and needs my help, but because God is always larger than we can imagine.

As we minister to and relate to those of other faiths, we become more authentic and faithful Christians

If sin is, as Luther said, "cor curvatus in se," ('the heart curving in on itself'), our vocations should stretch our hearts. The Christian Scriptures offer many examples of people who were sent to love and serve those who were not only 'strange' and 'different,' but were the very ones despised and seen as problematic by the ones God sent. Jonah comes to mind.[8] The very act of hearts being stretched to where they would not formerly go makes that act a profound experience. In Clinical Pastoral Education, such stretching experiences happen often. An African-American student chaplain who grew up in the Deep South is called to minister to a dying white man, also from the south. A conservative Christian is asked to pray with a Jewish family. In the concreteness of the moment, we exercise our faith (or our faith exercises us); and we follow our human vocations. We give up trying to be God, and we let *God* be God.[9]

We are called to be ambassadors for Christ

We are always witnessing, whether we like it or not. As pastoral caregivers who will be easily identified as Christians by those to whom we minister, our vocation will be one of offering the quality of love that we

---

[7] Luther wrote about *simul iustus et peccator* in many places. One such place is in his *Against Latomus: Luther's Works* (St. Louis: Concordia Publishing House, 1955), Volume 32, 190ff.

[8] For an excellent discussion of the book of Jonah that is relevant to this discussion, see Jacques Ellul, *The Judgment of Jonah* (Grand Rapids, MI: William B. Eerdmans, 1971).

[9] Philip S. Watson, *Let God Be God: An Interpretation of the Theology of Martin Luther* (Philadelphia: Fortress Press, 1966).

have experienced in the Gospel to all those who struggle with illness, pain, and calamity. "See how they love one another," said Tertullian in the third Century about Christian communities.[10] In order to be effective, this love must contain tact and sensitivity, as well as respect for the other person and his or her faith. As ambassadors we must learn to live in a strange land in a respectful, peaceable way, trusting that there will be opportunities, when asked, to share about 'the hope that is within us, with gentleness and reverence.' (1 Peter 3:15).

In conclusion, Luther's words most dear to those who carry his name (a practice I doubt he would condone) are "pecca fortiter," or "sin boldly." In this brief essay, I have tried to "sin boldly" in the same sense that I imagine Luther did when composing his 95 theses, putting his convictions into the context of the accepted docrine of his day, so that current religious practice might be improved through the hoped-for dialogue within his faith community. I do so, knowing that, if I have erred, God will forgive me, and if I haven't, God will still forgive me.

---

[10] Tertullian, *Apology*, Chapter 39:7 Loeb Classical Library Series, volume 250, 1998.

Part 3

Other windows to competent ministry practice

A chaplain reflects on caring for a Jewish family

William H. Griffith

It was Saturday evening when my pager contact informed me of a need at one of our palliative care units. When I heard the name of the patient, I immediately suspected that he might be Jewish.

I wanted to be prepared to provide them the option of having a Rabbi so I checked my resource listings for that area and located the name of the Rabbi who was to be on-call for that weekend. As I drove to the facility my mind began to sort out the kind of spiritual support I might anticipate providing. This is a normal process whenever I am paged to the bedside of a dying patient, and as important as it is to be prepared I know that it is rare that what I anticipate is actually what I end up doing. I believe that each visit must be approached with an open mind and a flexibility that allows the caregiver to 'go with the flow' of the particular situation and appropriately improvise for the sake of timely and adequate care.

On this occasion I found myself hoping that they would be pleased that I had the name of a Rabbi that would be available on a Saturday night. Then, again, I thought they might be Jewish in name only and not even be interested in a Rabbi. What would I do if that were the situation? And if they were deeply religious Jews what would they expect from me as a hospice chaplain? What spiritual support would they expect from a non-Jewish, Protestant, Baptist chaplain?

I then realized that what I was really deeply concerned about was what I

William H. Griffith, D.Min., recently retired as a chaplain for the Hospice of South Central Indiana, Columbus, Indiana. Much of the content of this essay appeared in Griffith's book, *More Than a Parting Prayer: Lessons in Care Giving for the Dying* (Valley Forge: Judson Press, 2004), chapter 14—"Honor the Care Receiver's Faith"—pp. 56–58. Rev. Griffith graciously accepted our invitation to further document for us his reflective process on the ministry event involving a pastoral visit with a Jewish family. Griffith's comments *in italics* are meant to enable the readers to have some insight into his pastoral reflection as an interfaith chaplain providing care for that family. (The editors)

had to offer this Jewish family. I knew that my Christian beliefs based on the teachings of Jesus' life, death, and resurrection, if verbalized, were helpful when providing spiritual care to a Christian, but would not be appropriate for caring for a Jewish family. I would need to use Old Testament scripture which was familiar and remind them of the healing truth they needed to affirm. I began to think about the many Old Testament verses that I used in officiating at Christian funerals and concluded many of them would be appropriate.

When I arrived at the patient's room, I found it to be filled with family members. The young men were wearing yarmulkes (skullcaps).

When I saw all of the yarmulkes I knew immediately that the family requesting me was not only Jewish, but were probably very religious. I thought they would surely want the Rabbi, and I was so pleased that I had thought to find his name and knew how to reach him.

A woman with gray hair who was standing by the bed looked at me as I entered the room; I concluded that she was the wife of the dying man. I introduced myself to her, and she said, "Pastor, thank you for coming. Jacob is not going to make it and we need you to be here."

I was a bit surprised in hearing her call me 'Pastor' but it did signal that she was aware of my role as a clergy of a different faith tradition. Her immediate comment that she knew her husband was dying and it was important for me, a non-Jewish clergy, to be there with them made me feel very welcome. It also signaled an expectation which I needed to clarify.

Not that there was much doubt, but I confirmed with them that they were Jewish and then asked if it would be helpful if I contacted a Rabbi for them.

I actually had the hope that they would be very pleased that I could do that and, if she said yes, then my support for this Jewish family would be successful.

The woman smiled and said, "No, our God is your God, and he hears our prayers."

Well, that meant she didn't expect me to call a Rabbi, and that she was content that I was there with them. Her statement 'our God', I believed, was also meant to signal to me that her belief in God was compatible with my belief in God, and the presence of a Rabbi would not be necessary for her to experience spiritual support. That of course was her way of informing me that she knew I would provide the pastoral care she needed. This is the moment in the visit when all the anticipation of what might happen and what one might do is left behind. It is the moment that specifically initiates the process of providing the spiritual care that is expected.

I affirmed her statement and, since Jacob was not responding, I asked her if he had the assurance of God's love and care in these dying days.

She smiled again and said, "Oh, yes, he knew."

One of the common values that religious faiths share is the belief in a God of love, and knowing the Jewish teaching of the Old Testament, I felt it was a good place to start. This also gave me the opportunity to call the dying patient by name and therefore include him in our conversation. It is important not to ignore the non-responsive patient, because the medical profession informs us that hearing is the last sense to go and, in any case, a non-responsive patient needs to be treated with the same respect as any person who is able to respond in detectable ways.

I then was introduced to every person in the room, and the woman directed a grandson to get me a chair so that I could sit with her by the bed.

This gesture was another clear signal of the woman's expectation of the chaplain. She was not simply looking for a prayer to be offered by a religious clergy person as a ritual needed before the death occurs; she was expecting a person to provide some support by their presence. The offer of a chair meant this would be 'more than a parting prayer.' I knew that my sitting down by the bedside with the wife of the dying man would bring a direct focus on me, and they would all have some expectation of what would happen next. It was at such a time that I had to make a decision as to what spiritual care was expected and needed, and how I would provide it. Based on my assessment of expectation and need, I knew there were two basic directions that I could pursue. I could either start directly with the scripture, assuming I would choose those verses that would address their needs and expectations, or I could start with the present moment and listen for those needs to be clarified before drawing upon scriptural support. I don't believe there is simply a right or wrong way to proceed, but the personal assessment of the moment must determine the direction to be taken. It is much like preparing a sermon in that the preacher may start with a biblical text and amplify and apply it to life experience; or start with the latter and then shed light on the life experiences with the scriptures.

My choice in this situation was to start with the present moment of the people in the room who were all family and were all there to support one another while they all faced together the dying of someone they loved. They were all calm with no one showing any extreme emotion of grief, and the way they treated one another showed me their relationships were very caring.

I sat down, and I invited the people in the room to tell me about Jacob as they knew him. Different ones spoke up, telling me about their relationship with him and sharing some little remembrance of how special he was to them. There was laughter as they remembered things that had happened or lessons they had learned.

I have found that this exercise of remembering is important to all persons re-

gardless of the faith that supports their spiritual journey. This life review exercise enables persons to celebrate the life of the dying as they desire to remember him. Inviting them to tell their stories is a way they support one another in affirming the relationship they have had with the person who is dying. This also enables them to introduce the one dying to the chaplain who does not know him. In that particular pastoral visit, it provided insights into his life of faith, his love for others, and his service to the community. These insights could then be woven into the content of a prayer of thanks offered on behalf of the family for the one who was dying. The chaplain facilitates this process by the questions that are asked to encourage people to share their stories. Their sharing also provides the chaplain with needed insights into what scriptures may be helpful for them as they continue their grief journey together. It is important for the chaplain to have knowledge of scriptures that can be identified as the stories are told, so that they may be shared at the appropriate time.

An hour passed so quickly, and when I felt the time was appropriate, I stood and told them how special it was for Jacob and his wife to have such a loving family present at such a time.

Knowing the opportune time to bring closure to a spiritual support visit is essential. The sense of the appropriate time must be based on what is happening in that room with those present for the occasion. All too often spiritual caregivers conclude a visit at a time that is more fitting to themselves, and often it is because they have become uncomfortable with the conversation among those who are present. Caregivers who feel inadequate and uncomfortable in dealing with death and dying issues need to examine their own feelings and know where their comfort or discomfort lies. Knowing when to offer a closing prayer is very important, and such a time should not be used as a way to exit an uncomfortable situation. It is also expected that the caregivers turn off cell phones or pagers so that their ministry to person or persons does not get interrupted making the ones being cared for feel disrespected or like someone else has a more important need than they do.

I knew the appropriate time had come because everyone in the room had spoken and all seemed content with the invitation given them to tell their stories. The wife who had requested the chaplain was also expressing thanks for the stories and what they meant to her.

I encouraged them to keep telling their stories and to tell Jacob how much he meant to them. I usually conclude my visits with a prayer, and I wanted to be sensitive to how I, a Baptist, could best minister to this Jewish family, so I asked them if I could leave them with a prayer and a blessing from the Old Testament.

The ministry I provided this family was essentially a ministry of spiritual presence. This is the kind of ministry that is often difficult for clergy who are so accustomed to 'doing' more than they are 'being.' I was very much aware that I had been invited to be a presence with them, and I was not being looked to for answers to their spiritual questions. Spiritual caregivers need to be reminded that ninety percent of caregiving is just genuinely being there, and once there allow the next ten percent to be determined by those who are present.

All of the pre-visit anticipation I had about this visit was a good exercise in identifying the potential areas of need as well as resources available, but allowing the situation to shape the spiritual support offered was the key. The ministry of presence included selecting scripture verses that affirmed the importance of God's presence with us, and using only those scriptures that were grounded in their faith.

They agreed this would be very good, so I read to them the twenty-third Psalm, offered a prayer, and then blessed them with the benediction from Deuteronomy 31:8: "It is the Lord who goes before you. He will be with you; he will not fail you or forsake you. Do not fear or be dismayed."

One can hardly go wrong with this beautiful well-known scripture and I chose it because of the promise I wanted to affirm regarding God's spiritual presence. After reading the Psalm, I made a comment on the verse: "Even though I walk through the valley of the shadow of death I will fear no evil because you are WITH ME." I made the emphasis that I personally felt that this was one of the greatest truths in all of the scriptures, the truth that God is always trying to convince us that we do not face the uncertainties of life alone. God is with us. It is here that I knew it would not be appropriate to include my personal affirmation of this truth by telling them how wonderful it was that God even gave the name Emmanuel to Jesus! That is my belief and not theirs. What I intended to do was to affirm that truth from the perspective of their teachings, without raising controversy over my own convictions. At such a time I do not feel that I am compromising my convictions by affirming theirs, especially when those truths are woven into the fabric of my own faith, and are read from my own Bible.

When I offered the prayer I was able to verbalize gratitude to God for the man, Jacob. I was able to include specific words of praise that I had heard spoken during the time of story-telling. I was able to be very personal at a time when I did not even know the person about whom I was praying. The community of family was the community of faith in those moments of connecting us all with God. Knowing the life of the biblical Jacob I was able to make some positive comparisons with the Jacob who was dying, and by doing so, connect him to the one for whom he was named. I also concluded my prayer in a manner that would not be offensive to the Jewish family. I quoted the familiar words, "Hear our prayer O Lord, incline thy ear to us and grant us thy peace. Amen." As an interfaith chaplain, I do not feel it is necessary for me to end all prayers "in

Jesus name." but in a manner that is appropriate both for me and also those with whom I am praying. This communicates something of respect for those who have invited me to care for them, and support them on their journey.

The scripture I chose for a blessing and benediction for the family was from their Torah and it too carried the affirmation of the importance of spiritual presence, and of our God being with us. This is a verse that came to mind because I have often used it at the time of funerals when persons gather and are overcome with grief. Having available resources from a variety of spiritual experiences is very important. They do not always have to be memorized, but knowing where to find them is crucial when time is of the essence.

As I rode the elevator to the lobby, I was very much aware that I had just experienced a special moment unlike any I had ever experienced before. I was able to facilitate a meaningful closure with people whose religious experiences were in some ways similar and yet very different from mine. At the same time I had been blessed by that Jewish family. It was affirming to know that being sensitive to the belief system that has given people hope through the years makes it possible to connect with them in a very special way.

Further lessons for caregivers

Caregivers will discover that those people who have had a meaningful faith experience in life are most often the best prepared to accept death. The teaching and inspiration by which they have lived provides them with an inner confidence and trust at the time of death. They have lived a lifetime of values and beliefs that have provided them with assurance and the knowledge of God.

The interfaith caregiver has a unique opportunity to enter the lives of persons and provide them the opportunity to examine those spiritual values that have shaped a person's life. Chaplains are usually called upon when persons are confronted with some form of physical crisis. At such a time a person's beliefs and values can be a major source of spiritual support for their suffering.

"Voices of suffering—especially the voices of those who know they are dying and their families—become poignantly focused. Along with asking challenging questions regarding prognosis and other 'medical' inquiries, they become seekers and purveyors of 'spiritual' understanding and wisdom."[1] Chaplains have the unique challenge and opportunity to journey with such persons by becoming a pastoral presence and providing

---

[1] Keith G. Meador, "Spiritual Care at the End of Life," *North Carolina Medical Journal*, 65: 4 (July–August 2004), 226.

support for them.

Jacob and his family shared such a faith experience. Caregivers who participate in this kind of situation must recognize that their first priority is to invite the family to examine their beliefs and then to take the opportunity to affirm those beliefs as the family's needed hope and support. Caregivers need to remember that they are not there to change the family's beliefs if they differ from their own. Regardless of the label they put on their meaningful religious experiences, when people are able to articulate their beliefs with confidence and trust in a God who loves them, caregivers should affirm them by seeking a common ground where their faith traditions intersect. In my situation, my faith and the faith of the Jewish family was nurtured in the common ground of the Old Testament. From the Scriptures we both knew and valued, we were able to hear the Word of God for us in that moment.

I would remind all caregivers that what we do and say should be for the good of the dying patient and his or her family, and the attitude we bring to such a moment will shape the quality of our caring. It is an attitude that consciously remembers that whatever we do and say, it must be all about the mourning family and *their* personal faith values, not about us and our beliefs.

I cannot emphasize enough the importance of being open to those for whom we are called to care, and allowing them to share where they are so that they set the agenda for what we have to offer. A good biblical model for this approach to making available a spiritual presence is the New Testament story of the disciples on the road to Emmaus. It is a story that has a variety of meanings, but taken in its original setting it is a story of grief, and how someone cared for and enabled them to come to terms with their own faith beliefs. The one who cared for them joined them on their journey and asked questions that enabled them to open up and share how they felt, and what they believed. He used what they offered to assist them in clarifying their faith values and processing their grief. The end result of such caring was "their eyes were opened" and they became aware of a special spiritual presence that had cared for them. I believe a similar experience happened with the Jewish family, and happens often, as we join people where they are in their suffering, confusion, pain and sorrow and allow them to tell us their faith story.

6

Explorations I:
Applying an interpretive framework
Daniel S. Schipani and Leah Dawn Bueckert[1]

Our study of interfaith care situations has been enhanced by adopting and systematically applying a four-dimensional framework of analysis. We intentionally patterned the framework according to the structure of practical-pastoral theological reflection, and can describe it succinctly as follows:

- *Observe/describe*: what is going on in this situation? What are the key issues we can identify in this interfaith encounter, especially regarding the caregiver and her or his pastoral practice?

- *Interpret*: why do caregiver and care receiver behave and act the way they do? What is the psychological and theological signifi-cance of those actions? What is the caregiver seeking to accom-plish?

- *Judge*: what are the ethical-theological and pastoral-clinical norms at work in the situation (or, to what extent is the caregiver's min-istry truly effective and faithful?) Are there alternative norms that pertain in this situation?

- *Act*: what are some of the principles, in the sense of dependable guides for excellence in spiritual caregiving practice, which can be highlighted in light of this analysis?

In this chapter we illustrate one way of interpreting and judging a care-giving situation (steps 2 and 3 above) by applying a conceptual tool—the *grammar of transformation*[2]—that we have found to be particularly useful.

---

[1] The case material in this chapter is based on one originally presented by chaplain Russ Dewell for our seminar group study. We are grateful to Rev. Dewell for granting us permission to use it in this chapter.

[2] The conceptualization of the "grammar of transformation" is one of the contributions of the late theologian James E. Loder as presented in his book *The Transforming Moment*. 2nd ed. (Colorado Springs: Helmers & Howard, 1989), chapters 2 and 4.

The following case study was originally presented as an example of how chaplains often seek to "reconcile" their theological convictions with care receivers' different spirituality in sound ministry practice. The study of the case revealed that the situation may also be viewed as a case of reframing of the chaplain's initial assumptions coupled with his disposition to provide compassionate care (which actually facilitated the reframing). The next section presents the case as first brought to the seminar group followed by an appraisal of the case.

To bless and how to bless, Chaplain Jack's questions

The Child Birth Center rarely contacts the on-call chaplain with good news. This call was no exception: fetal demise, 28-week boy. "Would you come up to perform a blessing, chaplain?" the nurse asked. "Certainly. I'll be right there."

My sense of calling, theological education, and, most significantly, previous experiences with fetal demise automatically and naturally started informing and guiding me on how to proceed: what to watch for, issues to consider, what words might be caring, and so many words that would not be helpful. One thing I decided, we—the parents and I—needed to clarify was what "blessing" meant to them.

I wanted to be able to provide for them what they wanted (expected?) in this highly emotional and difficult circumstance so as to best give compassionate care and help them begin discovering meaning in the wake of their tragedy. So far so good. I was not forming an agenda of my own, except to frame the issue that was requested: "blessing."

However, theological education, doctrinal confession, and previous experience do not quietly lie around in my mind waiting for the first thing to come first (clarifying "blessing") before taking the next mental step, even though that step may not require education or, especially, doctrinal confession. This was no exception. Being a Lutheran, it was virtually instinctual that I wondered if "blessing" meant baptism to the parents, in even a remote sense. More than my being Lutheran, previous experience informed me that it is good to baptize deceased infants out of compassion for parents and respect for the mystery of sacramental ritual, even despite contrary doctrinal definitions about the necessity of such. I had never baptized a deceased baby before, but had been present when a Roman Catholic priest did so for parents and families in very similar circumstances. Did these parents want the same by asking for a "blessing?" I would have to wait and see. I was about to enter the holy place of the Child Birth Center room.

Alone in the room, sitting up in bed, was a late-30s-ish woman of oriental decent. I presumed Chinese.

C   (chaplain) "Hello, I'm Jack, one of the hospital chaplains."

P   (patient) "Hi Jack. I'm Jane."

C   "I'm so sorry for your loss. I'm here to help you through this in any way I can."

P   (Tearing up and weeping mildly.) "Thanks, I appreciate that."

C   "The nurse told me you want a blessing for your baby."

P   (quietly) "Yes, I do."

C   "It's my privilege to help you with that. I want to help you as best I can."

P   (quietly) "Thanks."

C   "Can you share with me what it means to you to have your baby blessed?"

P   (a little more strongly) "It's about the gesture."

C   "Does the gesture come from any particular tradition?

P   "No. I'm less religious than spiritual."

C   "I understand. That helps me know how to care for you. Thank you."

Our conversation turned toward her general situation until I departed the room while a nurse tended to Jane.

I faced an interesting question. Jane did not even remotely refer to baptismal language or baptism. Could I, in good conscience, perform what she *wasn't* asking for? Part of my question came from the fact that I did not have "fetal demise blessing language" at my quick reference and use. Another source of my question was whether I fully understood what she meant by "gesture," and "spiritual." I was not going to grill and examine this nice woman in this heart-breaking tragedy so I could feel good about what support I provided. However, did I have enough information to feel confident that I could provide something to meet her need? It was not a question of whether or not I would do this for her, especially since I had already begun a pastoral relationship with her. I cherished the opportunity to provide compassionate care in the face of Jane's pain.

I was only uncertain how my automatic baptismal reflex was going to meet her desire for an other-than-baptismal spiritual gesture. Then, I realized my assumption. Even though, from a theological perspective, it is unnecessary for Lutherans to baptize deceased babies, the common practice of doing so out of compassion for parents and respect for sacramental mystery had become my reflexive response to fetal demise. Once I clarified my own theological convictions in my own mind, the clarity I experienced was as if the skies had cleared on a gloomy day. I knew that the *Lutheran Worship Agenda*[3] included blessings and dedications for civil marriages, churches, organs, schools, cemeteries, homes, and so on. Why not a deceased baby? Why not a deceased baby indeed?

Of course I could meet Jane's need as a by-the-book Lutheran with a non-specific other-than-baptism blessing. While this might seem like a blinding flash of the obvious to many (even to me after this event) the intense emotions of an event such as this, especially as an unannounced shock of an on-call shift, lead chaplains to refer to and rely on what they know and what they have experienced. For a Lutheran in this case, what I knew *and what I had experienced* was, specifically, baptism. However, Jane's request for a non-specific spiritual gesture has expanded what I know, and now, what I have experienced: to gladly provide something outside of my theological views and ecclesial practice *in good conscience*.[4] Thus, I avoided going through the motions just to fulfill Jane's request like some chaplain chore to get over with.

Having internally negotiated these doctrinal and spiritual hurdles, I was ready to provide Jane with compassionate and meaningful care.

A short time later, Jane's baby boy was returned to her. She, two of her friends, another chaplain, and I shared a meaningful and moving blessed gesture that included prayer for the boy, Jane, her absent husband (who was traveling and would join her soon), family, and friends. I had "reconciled" my doctrinal views, common practice, and Jane's spirituality. Praise God.

The case revisited

We will now present the case again by adding the interpretive framework proposed and several reflective comments. By focusing primarily on the spiritual caregiver and the internal conflict situation generated by the call to bless a deceased child, the ministry encounter can be viewed as

---

[3] The *Lutheran Worship Agenda* includes a "Burial of the Stillborn" service. It has prayers and language that are easily adaptable to a blessing for a stillborn baby in a hospital setting without imposing Lutheranism on parents and families. I had forgotten about this service at the time of the call to Jane's care. I re-discovered the service in writing this vignette. It would have been very helpful to keep in mind in the midst of the emotions of the moment.

[4] Chaplain Jack emphasizes "in good conscience" as crucially important in all of his pastoral care ministry.

analogous to the unfolding of a creative and transformative process.

Conflict/Struggle in a context of rapport[5]

My sense of calling, theological education, and, most significantly, previous experiences with fetal demise automatically and naturally started informing and guiding me on how to proceed: what to watch for, issues to consider, what words might be caring, and so many words that would not be helpful. One thing I decided, we—the parents and I— needed to clarify was what "blessing" meant to them.

[*Perhaps the chaplain started with the assumption that his need to clarify what "blessing" meant, so that he could be helpful, was also the care receivers' first need.*]

I wanted to be able to provide for them what they wanted (expected?) in this highly emotional and difficult circumstance so as to best give compassionate care and help them begin discovering meaning in the wake of their tragedy. So far so good. I was not forming an agenda of my own, except to frame the issue that was requested: "blessing."

[*It seems the chaplain assumed that the care receiver needed to somehow "discover meaning"—a primarily cognitive activity—as, perhaps, their main need?*]

Scanning[6] in search of resolution

However, theological education, doctrinal confession, and previous experience do not quietly lie around in my mind waiting for the first thing to come first (clarifying "blessing") before taking the next mental step, even though that step may not require education, or especially doctrinal confession. This was no exception. Being a Lutheran, it was virtually instinctual that I wondered if "blessing" meant baptism to the parents, in even a remote sense. More than my being Lutheran, previous experience informed me that it is good to baptize deceased infants out of compassion for parents and respect for the mystery of sacramental ritual, even despite contrary doctrinal guidelines about the necessity of such. I had never baptized a deceased baby before, but had been present when

---

[5] The supplied subtitles beginning with "conflict in a context of rapport" highlight the phases of what Loder calls the *logic or grammar of transformation*, the structure and dynamics of which are analogous to those of the *creative process*. Not unlike scientific discoveries and creation of works of art, such process potentially leads to transformation. It is our view that, indeed, a kind of transformation process took place during the ministry work described and analyzed in this chapter.

[6] Interlude for "scanning" defines the second step in the logic of transformation. "During this phase the conflict is for a time put out of one's conscious attention; the creative unconscious then has opportunity to search beneath the surface of awareness for … patterns that allow the reenvisioning and resolution of the conflict." Loder, *The Transforming Moment*, 225.

a Roman Catholic priest did so for parents and families in very similar circumstances. Did these parents want the same by asking for a "blessing"? I would have to wait and see. I was about to enter the holy place of the Child Birth Center room.

Alone in the room, sitting up in bed, was a late-30s-ish woman of oriental decent. I presumed Chinese.

C (chaplain) "Hello, I'm Jack, one of the hospital chaplains."

P (patient) "Hi Jack. I'm Jane."

C "I'm so sorry for your loss. I'm here to help you through this in any way I can."

P (Tearing up and weeping mildly.) "Thanks, I appreciate that."

C "The nurse told me you want a blessing for your baby."

P (quietly) "Yes, I do."

C "It's my privilege to help you with that. I want to help you as best I can."

P (quietly) "Thanks."

C "Can you share with me what it means to you to have your baby blessed?"

P (a little more strongly) "It's about the gesture."

C "Does the gesture come from any particular tradition?

P "No. I'm less religious than spiritual."

C "I understand. That helps me know how to care for you. Thank you."

[*Alternative responses by the chaplain might have been: "I see. I wonder, what do you wish for your child as I bless him?"; or "What would you like to happen because of the blessing?"*]

Our conversation turned toward her general situation until I departed the room while a nurse tended to Jane.

[*Here the chaplain could have engaged more the spirituality of the patient as a step towards nurturing her own healing and well-being. From the conversation provided, we don't know what her sense of need was, her hopes and her resources; neither do we know what kind of sense of the Holy or transcendence she had, sense of meaning, community and so on. Without that kind of information, it is difficult for chaplains to effectively visualize desired outcomes with or for the patient. It is also difficult to visualize pertinent pastoral interventions or*] *to (eventually) evaluate to what extent pastoral care was effective.]*[7]

I faced an interesting question. Jane did not even remotely refer to baptismal language or baptism. Could I, in good conscience, perform what she *wasn't* asking for? Part of my question came from the fact that I did not have "fetal demise blessing language" at my quick reference and use. Another source of my question was whether I fully understood what she meant by "gesture," and "spiritual." I was not going to grill and examine this nice woman in this heart-breaking tragedy so I could feel good about what support I provided. However, did I have enough information to feel confident that I could provide something to meet her need? It was not a question of whether or not I would do this for her, especially since I had already begun a pastoral relationship with her. I cherished the opportunity to provide compassionate care in the face of Jane's pain.

[The ministerial impulse and desire expressed by the chaplain was certainly key!]

Moment of insight (Bisociation[8])

I was only uncertain how my automatic baptismal reflex was going to meet her desire for an other-than-baptismal spiritual gesture. Then, I realized my assumption. Even though, from a theological perspective, it is unnecessary for Lutherans to baptize deceased babies, the common practice of doing so out of compassion for parents and respect for sacramental mystery had become my reflexive response to fetal demise. Once I clarified my own theological convictions in my own mind for myself, the clarity I experienced was if the skies had cleared on a gloomy day. I knew that the *Lutheran Worship Agenda*[9] included blessings and dedications for civil marriages, churches, organs, schools, cemeteries, homes, and so on. Why not a deceased baby? Why not a deceased baby indeed?

Of course I could meet Jane's need as a by-the-book Lutheran with a non-specific other-than-baptism blessing. While this might seem like a blinding flash of the obvious to many (even to me after this event) the

---

[7] One of the best resources to strategize spiritual care (in terms of both "assessment" and "intervention") is found in Larry VandeCreek and Arthur M. Lucas, eds. *The Discipline for Pastoral Care Giving: Foundations for Outcome Oriented Chaplaincy* (New York: Haworth Pastoral Press, 2001).

[8] Bisociation is the basic unit of an insight. The terms refers to the "surprising convergence of two incompatible frames of reference to compose an original and meaningful unity." Loder, *The Transforming Moment*, 222.

[9] The *Lutheran Worship Agenda* includes a "Burial of the Stillborn" service. It has prayers and language that are easily adaptable to a blessing for a stillborn baby in a hospital setting without imposing Lutheranism on parents and families. I had forgotten about this service at the time of the call to Jane's care. I re-discovered the service in writing this vignette. It would have been very helpful to keep in mind in the midst of the emotions of the moment.

intense emotions of an event such as this, especially as an unannounced shock of an on-call shift, lead chaplains to refer to and rely on what they know and what they have experienced. For a Lutheran in this case, what I knew *and what I had experienced* was, specifically, baptism. However, Jane's request for a non-specific spiritual gesture has expanded what I know, and now, what I have experienced: to gladly provide something outside of my theological views and ecclesial practice *in good conscience*. Thus, I avoided going through the motions just to fulfill Jane's request like some chaplain chore to get over with.

Release of energy[10]—Interpretation and verification[11]

Having internally negotiated these doctrinal and spiritual hurdles, I was ready to provide Jane with compassionate and meaningful care.

[There seems to be an implication or assumption here that, if the chaplain had not resolved certain "doctrinal and spiritual hurdles" he could not have provided compassionate and meaningful care. Could the reverse also have been the case: the disposition to provide compassionate and meaningful care facilitated such internal negotiation and resolution?]

A short time later, Jane's baby boy was returned to her. She, two of her friends, another chaplain, and I shared a meaningful and moving blessed gesture that included prayer for the boy, Jane, her absent husband (who was traveling but would soon join her), family, and friends. I had "reconciled" my doctrinal views, common practice, and Jane's spirituality. Praise God.

[Jane's main need was for support to cope with the loss of her child; the pastoral-priestly acts of blessing/praying undoubtedly served: (a) to validate the mother's wishes for her child (and for herself) and (b) to contribute to the necessary grieving process she needed to go through.]

Some time after this pastoral care event, chaplain Jack received a thank you card from the couple who lost their baby. They had named

---

[10] Release of energy and new openness is the fourth step in the logic of transformation in which the energy bound up with the conflict is released, and a new openness to the surrounding environment ensues.

[11] In order for the process to be completed, interpretation and verification are necessary. The chaplain needed to experience *congruence* as a subjective test of truth or good resolution of the internal conflict (that is, to what extent his sense of resolution was actually fitting in light of his initial dilemma). Further, the chaplain needed to experience *correspondence* in the sense of a public test of truth: his colleagues would judge whether a satisfactory resolution had indeed been achieved.

him Wayne as a way to connect them and him to their experience at the hospital. They wrote in appreciation of Jack's care ministry and his help in their decision to name the child, which had been significant in their healing process.

Further discussion

In a real sense, the group analysis of the case became a significant part of the final step in the *logic of transformation*, namely interpretation. We critically re-examined the whole caring event in order to help establish whether the chaplain's insights and actions had been appropriate. The seminar discussion of the case included consideration of the questions indicated below together with summary responses articulated as a result of our work together.

1. What assumptions, of their own and those of others, about sacraments, rituals, and/or practices do chaplains have to sort through to provide meaningful care when doctrine meets spirituality? That is, meaningful for the patient and the chaplain so neither is reduced to "going through the motions" of a rite contrived to fill the space of a pastoral visit.

   - On the one hand, it is not helpful to juxtapose or otherwise compare and contrast "doctrine" and "spirituality" because they belong to different categories (therefore, one cannot actually "reconcile" them as such either)

   - It is, on the other hand, helpful to seek "common ground" as much as possible, as implied in the statement "meaningful for the patient and the chaplain…." The vignette actually illustrates this point nicely because a real blessing[12] was experienced by care receiver and caregivers alike.

2. How do chaplains and patient(s)/families negotiate the best way to shape the requested and available sacrament, ritual, or practice?

   - Seeking the clarity provided by adequate spiritual assessment, and timely permission from the care receivers (patients and/or family members) are essential.

   - It is often possible to include the care receivers' input which in itself can be validating and empowering. For example, as suggested

---

[12] "Blessing" is here understood as the (mediated) bestowal of well-being or good upon the persons involved, including in this case the child's body. According to the vignette, the chaplains ministered authoritatively as mediators of Grace. They offered the blessing as a special expression of the shared hope that, indeed, child and mother would receive the wished-for gifts of well-being and peace through and beyond the experience of death and loss.

as an alternative response on the verbatim, the chaplain could have asked Jane what she wished for her child (and for herself, spouse, etc.) and make that a part of the prayer/blessing as appropriate.

3. What authority does a chaplain have, exercise, or abdicate to reconcile doctrine, practice, and spirituality? There are various sources and kinds of authority at play, such as:

- The authority that comes from the ecclesial body which either commissions, ordains, or otherwise authorizes pastoral care ministry in the hospital setting. The chaplain has therefore delegated authority, and she/he ministers as a representative of the church and/or denomination whether explicitly or implicitly. As such, the chaplain discerns and makes judgments, sometimes including consultation with either chaplains (or other caregivers) of different denominations or faith traditions, or with colleagues, supervisors or otherwise "authorities" of her/his church.

- The authority that stems from being authorized (and therefore also expected) by the hospital to provide competent and effective pastoral care service as a chaplain, whether employee, volunteer, or CPE student.

- The professional authority that stems from an integration of the above in terms of vocational commitment, personal character, and ministerial competence.

- The authority conferred by the care receiver (patient and/or family member) who welcomes or otherwise expects to be cared for adequately by the chaplain.

Explorations II:
Hawaiian chaplains reflect on interfaith care

A group contribution[1]

The following paragraphs present a sample of responses to a questionnaire that served as an introductory tool to the study of interfaith spiritual care. The questions have been shared with many colleagues who in turn reported on their consideration. Readers too may find these questions helpful for self-reflection and discussion.

1. What are the biggest challenges and opportunities you encounter in interfaith situations?

Martin Buber, in his seminal work on the "I–Thou" relationship, reflects a tension that can be of significance in the area of interfaith dialogue. Too often, the interchange that takes place in efforts to engage other belief systems reflects an "I–It" relationship. There are nuances of "being tolerant" which often diminish the personhood of persons and of the power of their faith. Too often "tolerance" is an easy way out of becoming engaged in a respectful process of "give and take." Tolerance has a way of placing a person or a "religion" on the fringe of our existence, to some extent, "out of sight, out of mind." There is no need to engage, to understand, to accept, and to love.

The biggest ongoing challenge I face is to resist the temptation to

[1] The material in this chapter consists of excerpts from a discussion of interfaith care involving Christian caregivers and Buddhist care receivers in Hawaii. Chaplains whose responses are included are Charles Card, Anke Flohr, Glenn Harada, Al Miles, Pearl Misa-Lau, and Kim Noble; all are ordained ministers. We gratefully acknowledge the contribution of Rev. Anke Flohr, for having led the discussion of these questions with several colleagues, and having sent us available written records. She also secured permission from the participants to include a selection of responses for publication. Anke Flohr, M.Div., was Director of Clinical Pastoral Education at Pacific Health Ministry, Honolulu, Hawaii. Currently she is the Professional Leader/Education Supervisor at Sunnybrook Health Sciences Centre, Toronto, Ontario, Canada.

either "Christian-ize" or "Westernize" the spiritual care situations in which I have the privilege of serving. Having been indoctrinated in American cultural and fundamental Protestant Judeo-Christian values, there is still a tendency on my part to assess and judge people through this very narrow lens.

Unfortunately, within most faith traditions, there are built-in doctrines, perspectives, values that automatically build barriers. The danger can be seen in the ministry in hospitals, where persons are in crisis and are most vulnerable, and we justify our "doing of ministry" in order that we can have access of "sharing Christ" with the person. Because Christianity claims to be "the way, the truth and the life" we feel justified in ignoring or even more pernicious, denigrating the person's personal faith, especially if the person is not a Christian.

One challenge in interfaith situations is working with patients of another faith who have perceptions and stereotypes of chaplains. They may feel that we cannot help them because we come from another faith background. They prefer to be ministered to by someone of their own faith. The opportunity for chaplains trained in interfaith ministry is that we know where to find resources to assist this person in need. Another challenge is ministering to those who have had negative experiences with religion. They tend to close themselves off from effective religious coping mechanisms in handling the struggles of life. Those with negative religious experiences tend to categorize good religious people they encounter as bad and who cannot be trusted. On initial pastoral visits, they may have a difficult time trusting the chaplain. It may take time to develop trust with the patient.

Often I feel uneasy and cautious. I am my biggest challenge. I am concerned about reading and understanding non-verbal messages and about being able to read between the lines.

The biggest opportunity I have encountered in interfaith situations is the receiving of many blessings when I allow myself to remain open to the mysteries and sacredness of teachings from people who embrace religious and spiritual traditions other than my own.

The most powerful modality of interfaith dialogue is through talking story … that is also true of how we engage cultures. If we start with our doctrine, we hinder the free give-and-take of true dialogue. It is important to find our common ground, the place where our humanity merges with the other and then we can begin the discussion of those issues that are critical to each faith and culture. There is great power in acceptance and in the art of listening. True dialogue happens in the minute events of the I–Thou relationships that are not based on knowledge and tolerance but in engagement and the risk of being true friends with persons of other cultures and faith perspectives.

2. What kind(s) of "spiritual assessment" do you practice?

I am most helpful to others as a faith leader when I allow those I'm called to serve to determine their spiritual course of action. I invite people to tell me what gives them hope, meaning and purpose; provide brief reflections or utterances on what they share; and then ask these individuals how they think I can best serve them. If prayer, readings, referrals, or other resources are determined or requested, I provide this information. But, I shy away from advice-giving.

I work with several models:

(a) The 7x7 Model for Spiritual Assessment developed by George Fitchett (*Assessing Spiritual Needs: A Guide for Caregivers* [Minneapolis: Augsburg, 1993]). He notes seven dimensions of "holistic assessment" (biological, psychological, family systems, psycho-social, ethnic, racial and cultural, social issues, and spiritual) and seven dimensions of "spiritual assessment" (belief and meaning, vocation and obligation, experience and emotions, courage and growth, ritual and growth, community, and authority and guidance).

(b) A shorter assessment model is "HOPE" (including, source of Hope, meaning, comfort, strength, peace, love and connection; Organized religion; Personal spirituality and practices; and Effects on medical care and end of life issues.

(c) The ADDRESSING model, especially applied with the staff and CPE students, developed by Pamela A. Hays (*Addressing Cultural Complexities in Practice* [Washington, DC: American Psychological Association, 2004]).

3. What kinds of "care interventions" do you consider most appropriate and why?

Ministry of presence works the best: empathetic and compassionate care with active listening. I need to be authentic, genuine, warm, real.

One of my spiritual tools is my ears which I use by listening to patients. I provide opportunities for religious worship. I pray for those who desire prayer. If they desire religious literature, I provide religious literature that is interdenominational. I have provided Mormon patients with the Book of Mormon. I ask Buddhist patients if they would like a Buddhist priest to visit them. Catholic patients receive visits by the priest and are offered sacraments and communion. If they desire, I make myself available to those with "no faith" and provide ministry of presence for them.

It is also essential that I work in partnership with a team of individuals from a wide field of professional disciplines: advocates, batterers' intervention specialists, child protective services providers, crisis intervention counselors, law enforcement officers, legal professionals, shelter workers, victim and witness assistance personnel, and other health care and spiritual care providers, to name just a few.

I have discovered over my four years of being a chaplain that in the beginning, I do not approach each person too differently. I listen and try to be respectful of his or her belief system. Establishing a relationship through listening, and consistency for those I visit over a longer period of time, are my key strengths in providing spiritual care for my patients, residents and family members.

Chaplains must ensure that the spiritual values of the patient are affirmed in a nonjudgmental way. We must respect the culture, ethnicity and religious preference of each patient. As chaplain, I am the primary spiritual caregiver to the patient and function in that capacity until the patient requests a change. At that time I inquire if the patient has a connection with local clergy and if he/she would like for me to contact anyone specifically. Then a referral is made to the spiritual caregiver of their choice.

4. What kinds of "good news" do Buddhist care receivers especially welcome or wish to receive?

I experience Buddhist residents and patients as very welcoming. Kindness and gentleness, open ears and mind, a listening heart, creating a space to share, have been appreciated. Respect without judgment.

The greatest assistance I can usually provide to people in need centers not so much on the words I offer, but instead on my ability to listen in silence to their sacred stories.

In my experience, Buddhist care receivers are among the most accepting and open group of individuals. I am often called to visit Buddhist patients and families at the medical center where I serve, even though the requesters know that I am a Christian pastor. This is especially true of health care colleagues who are Buddhist. The needs vary, but these requests commonly center on my offering a few compassionate words at or near the time of death, or during a funeral or memorial service.

Simple prayers are often appreciated, such as these [from the verbatim of a pastoral visit to a patient in the process of dying, with the husband and sons at her side]: "O God, we ask your help at this time. We especially ask that you would be with Mrs. N during her last moments. We pray that she is not in pain and that her transition from this life be gentle and peaceful. We pray that anything that may be burdening her would be released. We thank you for her family that is present … for their love and support of her. We pray that you would comfort them in their time of need and give them grace and strength for the moments and days ahead. We pray all of this in your name. Amen." In the same situation, a prayer after the death of Mrs. N (requested by her husband): "Dear God, we thank you that Mrs. N is no longer suffering and she has transitioned from this life into the next. Watch and care for her. God, we thank you for what she was to those who love her and we ask for your comfort for them as they grieve the loss of their wife, their mother, and their friend. May you grant all of us peace. Amen."

5. As a Christian spiritual caregiver, how do you evaluate theologically the interfaith situation as such and your interaction with the patient (and/or relatives) in particular?

The core value of my theological belief system centers on a God and Christ who love equally humankind from both genders, and from all cultures, races, religions, sexual orientations, socio-economic levels, and spiritual disciplines. Therefore, my spiritual care practice must model these same essential qualities.

Jesus is my teacher and model for healing relationship, love, dialogue, respect, and forgiveness. Through Christ we know that God reaches out in love to all. I am called to walk the path of holiness that Jesus showed me. He reached out to the Samaritans, "lepers," bleeding women, sinners, the poor. God shows the face of mercy and love. We must be subject to all human beings, servants, God's willing instrument. Jesus healed the ones in need, the marginalized. He loved them, ate with them, touched them, comforted them, blessed them, served them, encouraged them, taught them, and liberated them by his own suffering, death, and resurrection. Finally, Jesus breathed on them to infuse them with the power of the Holy Spirit. Jesus journeyed with people full of compassion.

I have no hidden agendas. No theological argument but about human sharing. Dialogue strives to eliminate defensiveness.

6. How do you characterize a fruitful (both effective and "faithful") practice of interfaith pastoral care?

From one's own spiritual tradition, we must assist or help patients and relatives engage their spirituality or religiosity in order to face their life and death struggles. Staff members must be educated on the importance of spirituality as a resource in handling the difficulties of life.

A fruitful practice of interfaith pastoral care must have at its core acceptance of and respect for all religious and spiritual traditions. I firmly believe that any religious beliefs, doctrines, and practices which espouse bigotry, hatred, male domination and female subjugation, violence, and any other beliefs that add to the oppression of other human beings or animals, need to be condemned. At the same time, all religious and spiritual traditions that practice and teach love, respect, and the equal value and worth of all humanity need to be embraced.

I look for "connection" in pastoral care. My caregiving is grounded in building relationships. I look for a sense of "meeting" each other. The "between" is the essential dimension.

Also important are knowing spiritual and religious resources available and knowing how to access these resources whenever needed for patients or staff. Interface with your staff and see if they are aware of spiritual issues of patients. Meet with Pacific Health Ministry chaplains and staff monthly to discuss interfaith ministry.

Over the years, I have become more adept at being short on speaking and long on listening to and learning from the experiences of people who espouse religious and spiritual traditions other than my own. In turn, colleagues from other religious and spiritual traditions have shared that they too have found it helpful to learn more about my religious upbringing and spiritual practices.

Explorations III:
An exercise in pastoral-theological imagination

Daniel S. Schipani and Leah Dawn Bueckert

This is the third and final chapter on alternative explorations in pastoral theological reflection that were considered in the seminar group we led at Lutheran Hospital of Indiana. It refers to an unusual activity that we devised after John Peterson[1] shared with us an excellent article from *The New York Times* on the ministry of Chaplain Peggy Muncie in New York City. The article is reprinted below with permission from the publisher.[2]

Offering comfort to the sick and blessings to their healers

By Jan Hoffman

At 1 p.m. on a weekday, the emergency department at St. Luke's-Roosevelt Hospital in Upper Manhattan is in full cry, with bays crowded, patients on stretchers lining the hallways, and paramedics bringing in more sick people. Time for the Rev. Margaret A. Muncie to work the floor.

Not shy, this pastor with the clerical collar, the Ann Taylor blazer and the cheerful insistence of one whose own mother called her a steamroller. Among the first women ordained an Episcopal priest and a self-described "Caucasian minority," she's an odd bird among the ethnically diverse staff and especially the patients, most of them black or Latino. But she keeps pecking her head behind curtains, parting gatherings of worried family members, impervious to startled looks of suspicion.

"Hi, I'm Peggy Muncie, a hospital chaplain," she says. "Would you

---

[1] As previously indicated, Rev. John D. Peterson is Pastoral Care Division Director at Lutheran Hospital of Indiana in Fort Wayne. He is also a CPE supervisor.

[2] The article was originally published in *The New York Times* on July 17, 2007.

like a visit?"

She's not there to thump. Deftly, she asks people how they're feeling, then lets them vent their pain and fear, their anxiety and frustration. She nods, a little pushy with her probing. She flags a nurse. "Can you direct a doctor toward that patient?" she whispers.

And always, at the end of a visit: "Would it be all right if I prayed with you?" The health care chaplain will touch a forehead, hold a hand and quietly pray worries to the Divine, speaking with inflections that, as needed, may be Pentecostal, Roman Catholic, Hindu, Jewish, Muslim. For the Baptist woman in Bed 7 whose anxieties are making her chest pain worse, the chaplain prays for calm to allow the medicine to work. Gradually, the patient's breathing slows.

"My job is to be present to patients without judgment," Chaplain Muncie says as she pumps a hand sanitizer, "and to help them find out what is meaningful to guide them through the stress of illness."

Most health care facilities around the country work with clergy members. But their involvement varies widely. Some hospitals merely have a list of on-call pastors; others retain professionally trained, board-certified health care chaplains, like Ms. Muncie, who is the only full-time cleric at St. Luke's. (The hospital also has a rabbi and an imam part-time, and a supervisory program for theological students.)

These varying levels of commitment have less to do with differing philosophies about spirituality and healing than with the bottom line. Insurance carriers do not reimburse for a chaplain's salary.

"We're a non-revenue-producing service, and in the economics of modern health care, that's not a good place to be," said the Rev. George F. Handzo, a vice president at the HealthCare Chaplaincy, a New York City organization that trains and places many chaplains.

"But there is a lot of indirect contribution to the mission of a hospital," he added, "as well as to its margin: customer satisfaction, customer retention and goodwill in the community. From a revenue standpoint, that's crucial."

The chaplain is also expected to minister to the hospital staff. As Chaplain Muncie, 59, makes her way throughout St. Luke's with a painstaking limp, she chats easily with doctors and nurses. She has sat with an intern who sobbed uncontrollably after pronouncing her first death and prayed with a ward clerk whose mother was in intensive care.

Every year, the chaplain performs a "Blessing of the Hands." She wheels a cart adorned with a tablecloth, flowers, a bowl and an MP3 player. Surgeons, nurses, aides crowd around as she dips their hands in water, blessing their healing work.

Although intercessory praying for the sick has existed since the time of ancient shamans, the chaplain's role now reflects the impact of modern technology on medicine. In her nearly five years at St. Luke's, Ms. Muncie has helped mediate "do not resuscitate" decisions, organ donations and bioethics disputes. After a visit, she puts the details in a patient's chart.

Now she's off to the intensive care unit, where many patients are intubated or comatose. Undeterred, Chaplain Muncie goes room by room, soul-searching. From one bed, eyes watch drowsily but intently; from another, a gurgle: "Ahhh," then, faintly, "mennnn."

"They say the last sense to leave is a person's hearing," she says. "Well, I was a cheerleader and I can belt it out as loud as anyone."

Spotting the chaplain, a woman jumps up from a bedside and embraces her. "Her husband is semicomatose," Ms. Muncie explains later. "She is going to be a widow soon and she knows it. She trusts me now, so I can begin to ask the difficult questions: 'Have you started to plan for your future?'"

One of Chaplain Muncie's signature responsibilities is to stand with a patient's family in the bleak early hours of death. The St. Luke's chaplains are paged when a child or a staff member dies; if a death is traumatic; or in the event of a calamity like a fire. But though raw, savage grief has no vocabulary, Chaplain Muncie must give it voice, in a multitude of languages.

Recently, a woman from Mexico who spoke no English had to be told that her eldest son, 16, had been stabbed, and died just after surgery. As Chaplain Muncie helped deliver the news, she realized that the shocked woman was Pentecostal. So the chaplain held her, praying in the name of Jesus that Jesus would take her son to Heaven, that Jesus would give her strength to bear this.

A few weeks ago, the chaplain had to prepare a Jewish family for a morgue viewing of their father. "I know that in Judaism, you don't say that the deceased goes to heaven," she says now. "You talk about memory and legacy. This family was having a hard time getting closure. So I said: 'What would your father be saying to help you get through this? What memory will you hold of him?' And their mood changed."

Her core belief about healing, says Chaplain Muncie, is animated by Psalm 121: "My help cometh from the Lord, who made heaven and earth"—spirit and body; faith and medicine. In 1996, doctors found a benign tumor in her brain the size of a tennis ball. The day after it was removed, she had a stroke. Her right side became paralyzed.

"I was frightened and mad," she says, over a hasty salad. "But mostly I worried about my husband and daughters: What about them?"

So many people prayed for her. She was not allowed to abandon hope, not through the years of pain and physical therapy that reduced the paralysis to a lurching limp, thanks to a device she was recently fitted for—"an electronic doohickey, my own little miracle."

She hitches up a pants-leg to show off the gadget, a neurostimulator. "I walk faster now," she says. "I'm the kick-butt chaplain." The experience deeply informs her ministry. "In Scripture it says, 'Get up from your bed and walk, your faith has made you well,'" she continues.

"'Well' doesn't mean perfect. But wholeness and healing can happen, even when there is still brokenness on the outside," she adds, tears spilling. "I'm more whole now than 12 years ago. But I still walk a little funny."

After lunch she visits the acute-care floor, sitting at the bedside of an 87-year-old glaucoma patient.

"The hospital can be a busy, lonely place," Chaplain Muncie says. "Who is there to walk this journey with you?"

The patient doesn't hold back. Brittle-thin, blind, she lives in public housing with her grandson, 19. But he's in serious trouble with the law. If she doesn't kick him out in three days, she says, she'll be evicted. The grandmother is heartsick about ejecting her grandson, yet terrified by looming homelessness.

The chaplain promises to alert a social worker. Immediately.

The patient pleads: "Would you call my grandson and ask him to visit? He hasn't been by."

The chaplain agrees. She gently mentions the parable of the Prodigal Son, of letting a profligate young man go so that he may one day return, mature and penitent.

Hands clasped, the women pray.

Chaplain Muncie stands to leave. "Oh, you lifted my spirit!" the patient calls out. "Will you visit me again?"

All seminar group participants read the article. We then discussed it in depth by focusing on the question, "How might Chaplain Peggy Muncie justify pastorally and theologically her spiritual care practices (especially prayers, blessings) with patients and staff of different faiths?" The activity was called an exercise in pastoral theological imagination. What follows is a summary of our response to the question.[3]

---

[3] We were able to get in touch with Chaplain Peggy Muncie, first by e-mail and then by phone in order to share with her about the seminar group experience and the use of the article as a testimony of her work in New York City. We also shared with her the responses to the question, "How

- First of all, Peggy Muncie is clear about her personal and pastoral identity: a 59-year-old, "Caucasian minority" woman, spouse and mother of two daughters; an ordained Episcopal priest who serves as pastoral caregiver at a hospital in Upper Manhattan. As a full-time chaplain, she is a member of the health care team which includes two part-time spiritual care colleagues, a rabbi and an imam. Her own experience of illness, hospitalization, suffering and loss, and recovery has been a transformative process that deeply informs her ministry.

- She is committed to always care *Christianly*, especially in the multifaith world of a health care center.[4] "Caring Christianly" is the kind of spiritual caregiving that stems from three key dimensions of the Christian faith: a particular vision of reality and the good life; a disposition to care as a form of love of neighbor-stranger inspired by Jesus Christ; and a sense of vocation to serve in partnership with the Spirit of God.

- Because of her faith and ministerial identity and vocation, this chaplain's prayers may be assumed to be implicitly offered "in the name of Jesus" even though she will not mention Jesus in her prayers and blessings for other-than-Christian care receivers and colleagues.

- We assume that Chaplain Muncie always offers to pray with and/ or for people for several reasons: (a) prayer is a universal, cross-cultural spiritual practice and faith language (although, for people of non-religious faiths, prayer may be neither significant nor desirable); (b) prayer is potentially good for spirit, soul, and body; (c) when she prays with and/or for people, she has an opportunity to give voice to the care receiver's heart, their hopes and desires; (d) when she prays, she can exercise multilingual competency by using spiritual or religious language familiar to the care receiver (while realizing that common language does not necessarily connote theological commonality, a realization that also pertains,

---

might [you] justify pastorally and theologically [your] spiritual care practices (especially prayers, blessing) with patients and staff of different faiths?" She graciously and enthusiastically engaged us in conversation, affirming much of what we shared and offering clarification and expansion on some points. We are grateful for having become acquainted with Peggy Muncie and her fruitful and inspiring ministry of spiritual care in a multifaith setting.

[4] In our phone conversation, Chaplain Muncie stated being deeply committed to Jesus Christ and ministering, in her words, as an "incarnationalist."

of course, when she prays with Christian care receivers!); (e) by offering prayer she seeks to communicate compassionate concern; by telling people that she will pray for them she communicates that she will remember them (and remembering is actually a key dimension of care).

- Praying can be emotionally and spiritually helpful. Chaplain Muncie always prays for herself and also regularly for patients and their families and colleagues, whether they know it or not. So the question for this caregiver is not, "should I pray for so and so …?" Rather, the question is, "when and how will I pray well for so and so …?"

- Performing a blessing (e.g. the yearly "Blessing of the Hands") is not only a *pastoral* act but a *priestly* one as well. When Chaplain Muncie blesses people she bestows grace on them as a representative of Divine Grace. She communicates affirmation of the care receivers and of their deepest longings for healing and wholeness. She seeks to be a blessing to those around her as she embodies the good news ("gospel") of healing and hope. She also thanks staff for the blessing they are to others.

- We might say that Peggy Muncie seeks to keep growing in pastoral wisdom in three dimensions: *being* (key to *presence*: "My job is to be present to patients without judgment …"; "standing with a patient's family in the bleak early hours of death"); *doing* (key to *guidance*: "and to help them find out what is meaningful to guide them through the stress of illness"; "she trusts me now, so I can begin to ask the difficult questions: 'Have you started to plan for your future?'"); and *knowing* (key to *understanding* in context: "My help comes from the Lord, who made heaven and earth," "… spirit and body, faith and medicine …").

- Chaplain Muncie knows that Christian pastoral caregivers must cultivate a theological understanding that is born out of their religious tradition. What sets pastoral or spiritual practice apart from other clinical and psychological practices is that very theological and ministerial identity.

- Chaplain Muncie does not see that her job as a Christian spiritual caregiver is to try to save people's souls so they may go to heaven. Her job is to minister according to the model of Jesus, so that people may suffer well, may heal as well as possible, and may also die well.

Further reflection and dialogue prompted by this exploration led us to design the following diagram. It is meant to represent the triangle assumed to be always present in interfaith pastoral care situations viewed from a pastoral theological perspective:

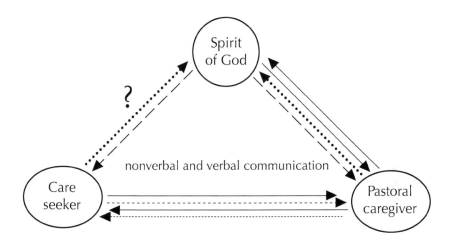

The arrows between care seeker and caregiver indicate the dynamics of nonverbal and verbal communication between us. The arrows linking Christian pastoral caregivers and the Spirit of God symbolize the communion that sustains and orients us as ministering persons. Such communion is experienced consciously as well as unconsciously (hence the arrows with broken lines).

The arrows between care receiver and God's Spirit indicate a fundamental theological claim we make: the Spirit's creating, liberating, healing and empowering work is already present in people's lives regardless of the shape and content of their (religious or nonreligious) spirituality, whether or not they would speak of a relationship with the Spirit of God.[5] In any event, from the perspective of the Christian pastoral caregiver, the relationship between care receiver and God's Spirit is assumed not as a problem to resolve but as a mystery to behold.

---

[5] In simpler terms, such a theological-anthropological claim is consistent, for example, with the Quakers' call to recognize the Light in any human being: "Do you respect that of God in everyone though it may be expressed in unfamiliar ways or be difficult to discern? Each of us has a particular experience of God and each must find the way to be true to it." *Quaker Faith and Practice* (Warwick, England: The Yearly Meeting of the Religious Society of Friends [Quakers] in Britain, 1999), Advices and Queries, chap. 1, no. 17.

Spiritual care in public and faith-based hospitals

Cornel G. Rempel

This essay starts with a characterization of chaplaincy as a special relationship, a service, and a discipline. The following sections consider professional standards, the place of chaplains within the health care institution, five operative dimensions of accountability, and the chaplain's image within the health care system. The final two sections, on the use of authority and power and the integration of the chaplain's role, include vignettes of interfaith spiritual caregiving in the hospital.

Relationship, service, and discipline

As a special *relationship*, spiritual care is a response to the spiritual need of another involving caring gestures such as a reassuring presence in the time of loss, a gentle touch in a time of pain, a prayer in time of need, a listening ear in time of confusion, the validation of another's emotions or cry of distress, or the celebration of new-found meaning. As such, acts of spiritual care may be planned or spontaneous and can be received from certified chaplains, volunteers, hospital staff and virtually any caring person.

As a *service*, spiritual care is the provision of support through structured activities such as initial visits, pre-op visits, communion, baptism, a smudging ceremony or an anointing. Such deliberate services are provided by persons who have been granted the authority to do so.

In the health care system spiritual care also functions as a *discipline* with defined ecclesiastical, professional and administrative accountability so that it is professionally recognized and organizationally connected to other professional disciplines. To do so with integrity it must be:

Cornel G. Rempel, M.Div., is a retired chaplain currently living in Winnipeg, Manitoba, Canada. He most recently served as Director of Pastoral Services and CPE Supervisor at Philhaven Behavioral Healthcare Services, Mount Gretna, Pennsylvania.

- Endorsed by and be accountable to the interfaith community.

- Recognized by the health care industry.

- Responsible to the administration of the institution.

- Accountable to a professional association through professional certification, adherence to its code of ethics and standards of practice.

In this chapter I will deal primarily with chaplaincy as a discipline, comparing and contrasting chaplaincy as a discipline in public and faith-based institutions. The term public institutions will refer to the broad range of government-operated facilities, university teaching hospitals, for-profit hospitals, and community-based not-for-profit hospitals. Faith-based will refer to institutions with religious affiliation. My intent is not to contrast the character of the institution but to focus on how public versus religious sponsorship may affect the position and function of chaplaincy.

The difference between chaplaincy in institutions with religious affiliation and public institutions is more subtle than obvious. The similarities are greater than the differences, for several reasons:

- The same professional standards apply to chaplaincy in public and faith-based institutions even though some services may differ.

- Public hospitals are not devoid of spiritual awareness, and faith-based hospitals deal with fiscal, ethical, and management issues that are similar to those of public hospitals.

- The significance of spiritual factors in healing is broadly recognized today apart from specific religious affiliation.

- Many staff members in public institutions are people of faith who are concerned about patients' spiritual well-being.

- The provision of spiritual care is mandated for all health care institutions by hospital accrediting bodies, so the provision of religious services is by no means exclusive to institutions with religious affiliation.

In this essay I will reflect on how public versus religious sponsorship may affect chaplaincy in regard to application of professional standards, the chaplain's place in the system, levels of accountability, the chaplain's image, the chaplain's use of authority, and integration of the chaplain's role in the institution. Similarities as well as differences will be touched on.

Professional standards

Professionals in most fields are certified by a professional body and, as such, are accountable not only to their employer but also to their professional association. The same cannot be said for clergy in general. Most pastors are accountable to their denominations. Some are accountable only to their congregations. Some ministers are self-appointed.

Because of the absence of common standards of practice among clergy, health care institutions for too long were reluctant to call on clergy because they did not know what they could expect from them. Consequently, the spiritual needs of patients were sorely neglected. The Association of Professional Chaplains (APC) in the United States and the Canadian Association for Pastoral Practice and Education (CAPPE) in Canada are the major professional associations that promote and grant board certification for chaplains in order to assure a common standard of practice even though their religious affiliations and roles will differ from institution to institution. Certification requirements include:

- A Master of Divinity (M. Div.) or equivalent.

- Ordination or endorsement for specialized ministry from a religious body.

- A minimum of four units of Clinical Pastoral Education.

- Demonstration of ministerial and professional competence through a certification process.

- Adherence to the professional code of ethics and engaging in ongoing professional development.

Specialized ministry to the spiritual needs of people who come from a wide range of religious backgrounds, or with no religious background, at a vulnerable time in their lives requires specialized preparation, ongoing professional development, and appropriate accountability in both public and faith-based health care institutions. For health care institutions, whether public or faith-based, to employ chaplains as directors of spiritual care who are professionally certified and have received interfaith endorsement, assures that the candidate is acceptable to the interfaith community and is professionally prepared. For an institution to disregard certification places it in the position of having to make judgments in an interview process that it is ill equipped to make. Can you imagine a hospital determining in an interview process whether a prospective surgeon is qualified to do surgery? The medical profession determines that issue.

Certification is also in the best interest of the larger faith community because it assures that the chaplain is prepared to function appropriately in a multicultural and multifaith context. Major public medical centers are almost certain to hire only board-certified chaplains in order to avoid the need to establish their own standards for chaplaincy, and in order to offer a level of service in spiritual care that is consistent with the standards of other disciplines in their institutions. Prisons, nursing homes, and retirement centers often opt to hire part-time chaplains without requiring certification for economic reasons. Faith-based facilities may also place greater emphasis on the chaplain's character and religious affiliation without regard for certification. Hiring uncertified chaplains, however, perpetuates a lack of clarity of what to expect from a chaplain.

Having said that, to demand that all spiritual care personnel be fully certified is unrealistic at this time. Persons with a variety of qualifications can provide a variety of valuable services very effectively. But for the service to be recognized as an authentic discipline, it must at least be directed by a fully certified chaplain.

Place in the system

Public institutions, whether for-profit or not-for-profit, are established to provide a service in the community. Faith-based health care and social service organizations are driven by a moral imperative that flows from the sponsoring body's identity and may be expressed through added value or by providing for the underserved who would otherwise be neglected. Religious motivation and history shape medical and spiritual care in faith-based institutions. This, in turn, affects chaplaincy in terms of the chain of command, the allocation of space, the integration of spiritual care in the system, and the scope of expected services.

Roman Catholic sisters, driven by a clear mission to care for the indigent and people with disabilities or addictions, have a long history of providing a broad range of health care services across the United States and Canada. These health care initiatives as well as those sponsored by the Lutheran church, the Salvation Army, Seventh Day Adventists, United Methodists and others unquestionably originated to provide for the underserved and included generous provision of spiritual care on a salaried and volunteer basis.

Mennonites established mental health centers after World War II in response to the compelling case made by Mennonite young men who served as conscientious objectors in the overcrowded and understaffed state hospitals. These men came back to their home communities saying, "There must be a better way." Their persistence and motivation resulted in the establishment of seven community mental health centers across the United States and one in Manitoba, Canada. Services were characterized by competence, compassion and respect. Chaplaincy in these centers focuses not only on providing spiritual care for clients but also on resourcing staff to promote best practice in behavioral sciences in the spirit of Jesus' nondiscriminatory, compassionate ministry.

The mission of hospitals with religious affiliation is driven by the moral and spiritual vision of their founders. Therefore spiritual care will be more central to the institution's mission; reporting to the chief executive officer is more likely; the chaplain and administration are more likely to speak a common language, making chaplaincy less subject to the vagaries of administrative changes.

The mission of public hospitals at best is driven by humanitarian values. In a public hospital, the chaplain is more likely to report to some-one lower in the chain of command whose responsibility for a variety of departments may place the spiritual care budget at greater risk when resources are limited. Transitions in administrative leadership also pose a risk if spiritual care as a service and as a budget item has to be justified each time administrative leadership changes.

In public hospitals the primary link of spiritual care as a department is with other disciplines whereas in faith-based institutions the primary link may be with administration. Public hospitals are more likely to view spiritual care as a profession and faith-based hospitals are more likely to view chaplaincy as a calling. About twenty years ago, when chaplains in a university teaching hospital in Winnipeg were negotiating work schedules, salary, and benefits, hospital administration encouraged them to join an existing union in order to standardize negotiations, because virtually all other staff were unionized. By doing so, the chaplains gained negotiating power. In a hospital with religious affiliation unionizing would undoubtedly be seen as secularization. Adding volunteer on-call time to regular work hours would be the more likely expectation, by virtue of the chaplain's calling.

Faith-based institutions typically have the added expectation that the chaplain will represent the mission of the sponsoring faith group and help to keep the institution's mission consistent with the religious values of the sponsoring constituency.

Accountability

Because chaplains serve in multifaith contexts in both public and faith-based institutions, it could be assumed that chaplains in public hospitals must compromise personal conviction to ensure the provision of non-discriminatory service, and that chaplains in faith-based institutions are prone to impose a religious bias. Chaplains themselves may at times be unclear on these matters. Indeed, chaplains do serve people of all faiths and those who claim no religious faith. The question is whether preserving the integrity of faith of the patient can compromise the integrity of faith of the chaplain. Put another way, how can the spiritual tradition of patient and chaplain and sponsoring institution be fully respected in an act of spiritual care? Does the provision of spiritual care on an interfaith basis necessitate compromise? The answer, in part, lies in an examination of the issue of accountability.

Most professions exercise authority and maintain accountability based on their professional credentials and their employment contract. For the chaplain, regardless of the type of institution being served, several additional dimensions of accountability apply. If properly adhered to, they can minimize misgivings on the part of the public and confusion on the part of the chaplain. The operative dimensions of accountability for the chaplain should be:

- **Personal** authority derived from the chaplain's sense of call.

- **Ecclesiastical** authority granted by the chaplain's faith community.

- **Interfaith** endorsement.

- **Professional** authority through credentialing from a professional association.

- Administrative authority based on the chaplain's job description.

Personal authority, based on a sense of call, must be exercised cautiously to guard against imposing self. Ecclesiastic accountability calls for appropriate faithfulness to the chaplain's religious tradition without imposing it on others. Endorsement granted by an interfaith body permits the chaplain to serve the full spectrum of clientele without apology. Professional accountability assures oversight in reference to standards of practice. Administrative accountability pertains to fulfilling the employment contract.

Proper accountability in each of the above areas in both secular and faith-based institutions serves to assure competent professional practice while avoiding compromise. Let me illustrate.

Suppose a chaplain scheduled for on-call duty is paged to neonatal care because a newborn is at risk, but the chaplain does not show up as promised. The failure to respond is a breach of agreement and therefore an issue to be dealt with by the administration.

If, on the other hand, the chaplain shows up but gets into an argument with medical staff about the treatment plan, this is an issue to be taken up in professional supervision because the matter pertains to professional practice.

If the chaplain comes and is asked to baptize the infant but declares that offering the sacrament is not appropriate, then the religious affiliation of the chaplain and that of the infant's family come into play. If the chaplain lacks the authority to baptize because of difference in religious affiliation, then the chaplain is professionally obliged to refer to someone who is able to provide the service. If, however, the chaplain and the family are of the same denomination and the chaplain determines that the circumstances prevailing in this situation do not permit providing baptism, then neither hospital staff nor professional peers can insist that the service must be provided. This is an ecclesiastical issue that must be handled by the chaplain's ecclesiastical authority.

Proper differentiation of authority in both public and faith-based hospitals assures that provision of nondiscriminatory spiritual services will happen while preserving the patient's and chaplain's integrity.

In a faith-based institution, there is an additional, albeit subtle, level of accountability to the faith community that sponsors the institution. At times this adds weight to the services that are offered. At times it may impose expectation to preserve the moral code of the founders in a way that compromises the chaplain's objectivity in patient counseling. For example, in a hospital where abortions are not provided on moral grounds, the patient may not trust the chaplain to offer an unbiased hearing on a personal dilemma regarding her pregnancy.

The chaplain's image

In a public hospital the chaplain's identity may actually be kept in sharper focus than in a faith-based institution because the chaplain is seen more exclusively as the keeper of the spiritual keys. When an invocation is needed, the chaplain is called on to offer it. When a patient's religious beliefs conflict with medical treatment the chaplain is likely to be consulted. In an institution that is deeply rooted in a religious tradition the chaplain's role in reference to such services is less exclusive. Other staff may be just as likely to offer the invocation. They may claim equal authority in spiritual matters and feel less need to consult. As a result, the chaplain's education and expertise may inadvertently be underutilized. In public hospitals chaplaincy may be underutilized due to lack of recognition. In faith-based hospitals chaplaincy may be underutilized when staff claims equal authority to deal with spiritual matters.

As already stated, in a faith-based hospital the chaplain is more clearly linked to the founding mission of the institution than in a public institution. This may affect the patient's view of the chaplain. In my experience in Catholic hospitals, patients expected the sisters to make initial visits without a prior request for spiritual care. The visits were seen as hospitality calls with the intent of welcoming the patient into their care. In a public hospital the patient may initially contribute the motive of an unsolicited visit to evangelization or bearing bad news. The chaplain in a public institution may be seen as having a personal mission, and the chaplain in a faith-based hospital may be seen as representing the mission of the sponsoring faith community. The patient's willingness to accept the chaplain would then depend on the patient's image of the institution's sponsoring body.

Use of authority and power

Chaplains must pay attention to the use of authority and power. In any institution chaplains function on the basis of authority that is granted as well as trust that is earned through relationships. Formal authority is derived from the chaplain's position in the system. In a faith-based facility the chaplain may derive additional authority from the sponsoring faith group. On the one hand, if the chaplain exploits this conferred authority by converting it to personal power, that can raise resistance in staff, particularly when clinical decisions outside the realm of the chaplain's expertise are involved. Over-spiritualizing a psychiatric diagnosis in a behavioral health care setting would be a case in point. Arbitrarily interfering with medical treatment without due process would be another.

On the other hand, positive use of authority contributes to healing. The chaplain in a general hospital was called to the psych unit to see a middle-aged woman who had refused to eat for several days. Nursing staff observed that she had religious items on her night table so they decided to involve the chaplain in a last ditch attempt to avoid intravenous feeding. The chaplain found the woman rigidly stretched out on her bed with a blanket securely tucked under her chin and having a blank look. He introduced himself as the chaplain and gave her time to decide whether she would relate to this stranger. After a few moments she began to offer brief responses. When it seemed that some trust had been built the conversation proceded as follows:

Chaplain: I understand that you have not been eating your meals. I'm interested to know why you are choosing not to eat.

Patient: I want to die.

Chaplain: I'm sad to hear that. Could you tell me why you would want to die?

Patient: I want to die for Jesus.

Chaplain: And why would that be?

Patient: I want to die for Jesus because Jesus died for me. And by dying for him I will prove my faith.

Chaplain: Tell me, Agnes, why did Jesus die for you?

Patient: To save me from sin.

Chaplain: (In a quiet tone) And why would Jesus want you to die for him? Does he need to be saved?

Patient: (That question seemed to startle her. After a moment of reflection,) No, Jesus does not need to be saved.

(Agnes had been clutching a crucifix at her chest all the while and had claimed affiliation with the Ukrainian Orthodox church so the chaplain surmised that she would hold in high regard the authority of the clergy.)

Chaplain: (with a tone of authority) Agnes, I am a chaplain in the Protestant tradition and I want to assure you that Jesus does not want you to die for him. When Jesus died he counted on us to carry on the good work that he did for people. Jesus does not want you to die for him. He wants you to live for him.

Patient: (Agnes looked into space and pondered what she had heard. Then she slowly sat up and drank the glass of juice that was on her nightstand. The chaplain waited in silence.) I would like to have my supper now.

Chaplain: (Suppressing his gratification) I will ask the nurse to bring you a tray.

Patient: I would like to go to the lunchroom. (So chaplain and patient walked arm in arm to the lunchroom at the end of the hall where she was served.)

The next evening the chaplain was paged again because Agnes was refusing to eat. After brief encouragement she decided to have supper and abandoned her fasting after that. This encounter is an example of positive use of authority because the patient's change of heart resulted from the authority she granted the chaplain as a member of the clergy.

Authority and power,[1] whether derived formally or informally, must

---

[1] "Authority" and "power" are used in this chapter as very closely related but not as synonyms. *Authority*—whether conferred, earned, or taken—denotes the right or the "empowerment" to make certain decisions and to influence behavior in certain ways. *Power* means the actual ability

be exercised with discretion. The chaplain, in best practice, is actively engaged in the system, yet separate enough from the system to be a safe listener, a support, an advisor, and a confidant not only for patients and their families but also for staff. I often marvel at the depth of trust that can be earned and the range of influence a chaplain can exercise at all levels in the system. In the course of a day, the chaplain may offer spiritual support to the critically ill; comfort to families in grief; connect with staff, patient and family members in the dilemmas of difficult treatment decisions; participate in clinical care conferences; offer consultation to parish pastors; encourage members of staff; participate in bioethical decision making; conduct a memorial service; and respond to emergency codes. Acceptance and effectiveness develop from wise use of professional authority.

Integration of the chaplain's role

Spiritual care functions most effectively when it is integrated in the system, whether in public or faith-based institutions. Such integration is achieved first by a well-defined referral system in which the profession of chaplaincy is recognized and utilized as a discipline among disciplines. A second dimension of integration derives from the involvement of community clergy in the care of their parishioners while in the hospital and in follow-up care. A third dimension of integration goes beyond viewing spiritual care as a support service, to the intentional integration of spiritual care in the treatment process itself. The following case studies illustrate several dimensions of integration.

The first example comes from the medical unit of a general hospital. Bob was a 45-year-old male. His diabetes had reached a critical stage. Infection in his toes had set in to the extent that amputation might become necessary. Bob, however, refused all medication and treatment. He rebuffed attempts of persuasion from the physician and nurse, who were unable to treat him without consent. Recognizing that Bob was a religious person, the physician consulted the chaplain.

The patient's record indicated that Bob's religious affiliation was with a Protestant charismatic group. The chaplain offered to visit Bob without identifying the visit as a referral in order to avoid being dismissed on suspicion of collusion with medical staff. The chaplain focused on Bob's

---

to cause or prevent change. To use categories proposed by Rollo May, therefore, chaplains are "authorized" to use *nutrient power* (power "for") and *integrative power* (power "with") in dealing with care-receivers, as illustrated above. They must avoid using *manipulative or exploitative* (power "over"), and *competitive* (power "against") forms of power. Rollo May, *Power and Innocence: A Search for the Sources of Violence*. New York: Norton, 1972), 99–120.

need for healing rather than the physician's need for Bob's compliance. Bob welcomed the chaplain and declared that he was an itinerant minister in aboriginal communities in northern Canada. When the reason for Bob's admission to the hospital came up in conversation, the chaplain discerned that Bob was dealing with a crisis of faith.

The doctor is trying to convince me that I have diabetes, but I don't believe that.

You find it hard to accept what the doctor is saying.

I don't think it is serious. Besides, I have no need for a doctor. God can heal me without a physician.

So you want to entrust yourself to God for healing.

Yes. And if my faith is unwavering, it will happen.

Are you saying that accepting medical treatment would represent lack of faith on your part?

God has promised to do whatever we ask in faith. That is what I preach every Sunday.

And now you want to practice what you preach as a testimony to your faith.

Yes, and I count on God to keep his promise.

Bob, you go from one community to another in the north to preach the gospel. Why do you do that?

God has called me so that the people can hear the gospel message and be saved.

Why doesn't God save them without you?

[emphatically] God called me to proclaim his word. That is how God works. If I didn't preach, they would stay in their lost condition.

You believe that God won't save the people without your preaching but expect God to heal you without the physician. Do you suppose the physician could represent the hand of God in your healing just like God's message of salvation comes to the people through your preaching?

The chaplain left Bob to contemplate the question. On his visit the next day, the chaplain found that Bob was accepting treatment.

Another example is from a behavioral health context. Troubled by guilt, Jan sought help from a therapist in a mental health center. She was twenty-four years of age and engaged to be married. Now that she anticipated marriage and a family, she was deeply troubled by a decision she had made at the age of eighteen to terminate a pregnancy. It was evident to the therapist that Jan was dealing not just with psychological issues but also with a crisis of faith. The therapist dealt with spiritual and psychological dynamics in helping Jan come to terms with her guilt, but it appeared that Jan needed to seal in her heart what she had come to terms with in her mind.

The therapist was a man of faith who could have initiated a religious ritual of closure, but he recognized that involving a chaplain at this point would introduce an added dimension of spiritual authority. With Jan's permission, the therapist discussed her situation with the chaplain. The chaplain then arranged for Jan and her fiancé to come to the meditation chapel and bring an object that would represent the lost fetus. He also suggested that she prepare a written statement or a prayer to express what she felt she needed to say. The chaplain invited the therapist to be present for her support and as a sign that the therapy sessions and religious ritual were components of the same therapeutic process, rather than separate events.

The ritual included carefully selected scripture readings and prayers. At a given point, Jan approached the altar and addressed God and her terminated fetus with a tearful confession. Then she placed the rose she had brought at the foot of the cross and left it there as a sign of leaving her lost fetus in the care of a loving God. This act was followed by the chaplain's words of absolution and assurance of forgiveness.

To regard Jan's burden only as a spiritual issue would have been ineffective, because a premature ritual of closure would not have resolved her conflict. The psychological issues also needed to be addressed. However, cognitive therapy alone was not enough to assure healing either. The therapist's recognition that the issue was both psychological and spiritual made Jan's healing more complete. This event represented wholesome integration in that neither the therapist nor the chaplain acted in isolation.

In the first example, separation between the chaplain and the physician was needed to neutralize Bob's resistance. In Jan's case, the presence of the therapist in the ritual of closure was important to symbolize the integration of the psychological and the spiritual in the healing process. Such integration may happen more naturally in a facility with religious affiliation where it is likely to fit with the culture of the institution. But it can be done in a public institution as well, based on relationships built between chaplains and the clinical staff.

The previous examples represent integration at the professional level. The following examples represent integration at the systemic level. A middle-aged woman escaped from the psych unit of a general hospital and walked into the nearby river to commit suicide by drowning. Staff members felt devastated and asked the chaplain to place the call to the family. The chaplain met the family when they arrived and joined them in their meeting with staff and provided follow-up care for the family. Several days later staff engaged in a clinical review of this tragic event. Among other things, the review resulted in drafting a new policy on steps to be taken in the event of a suicide. The policy included a clear definition of the chaplain's role in relation to family and to staff in the event of a suicide.

A final example comes from the intensive care unit where it was determined that a male patient showed no brain activity after repeated tests. Family was in agreement that life support be discontinued but the timing of that was not specifically discussed. The chaplain was called when the man's son arrived forty-five minutes after life support had been discontinued. The chaplain learned that the respirator had been turned off at about the time the son arrived at the airport from across the country. With a delay of only forty five minutes the son would have experienced his father's death in a very different way than he did now. He had come a long distance only to miss an opportunity to sit with him and speak words of affection even if his father could no longer respond.

Determined that this should not happen again, the chaplain arranged with medical staff that whenever a decision was made to remove life support a chaplain should be called prior to carrying it out because at that point they were no longer dealing with a medical situation but with a family situation. The chaplain would meet with family to assess their readiness to let their loved one go, and determine if anyone else should be there before it was carried out. The chaplain would then offer the family the opportunity to gather around the bed for their final farewells and for a prayer of release. When all family members had drifted back into the family room and felt sad but satisfied, then the chaplain would notify staff that they could proceed to turn off the respirator.

Discontinuing life support is not pleasant for anyone. By following this protocol, not only would the family be helped to achieve closure but medical staff would be helped as well by being assured that the family was at peace and that the removal of life support was a completion of what the family had already done in the ritual of release.

In the case of the suicide by drowning, the chaplain's role was written into the psych unit's policy and procedure manual. In the intensive care unit the agreement was verbally made and maintained through regular practice. In both cases the chaplain's defined role in the treatment team was based on chaplaincy being recognized as a discipline rather than as only a random act of care.

Conclusion

Spiritual care is provided through caring relationships as well as established services and, in its fullest dimension, functions as an integrated profession within the system. In both public and faith-based hospitals chaplaincy focuses on providing spiritual care, not in reference to a particular tradition, but in reference to people's need. Nondiscriminatory spiritual care requires that we draw on our own spiritual resources as we help people access theirs. But in specific needs that pertain to the patient's religious tradition we don't have to be all things to all people. In fact we violate them when we try. For the chaplain to refer specific needs to the most appropriate spiritual caregiver is as important as it is for medical staff to refer to the chaplain.

Common standards of training and common standards of professional practice minimize differences in the delivery of spiritual care between public hospitals and faith-based institutions. However, the religious and cultural orientation of an institution affects the way spiritual care is recognized and supported.

In the future, increased attention to cultural diversity may make differences more noticeable between institutions of different types. Some public hospitals have chapels that feature specific worship centers appropriate for various religious traditions. Some provide a suitable space where a smudging service can be provided without setting off the fire alarm. Chapels in hospitals with religious affiliation will more likely continue to reflect the tradition that sponsors the institution without denying others the opportunity to worship. Public hospitals will tend to focus on *spiritual* care more generically, while hospitals with religious affiliation will likely retain a more specific focus on *pastoral* care. Nevertheless, with growing public interest in alternative medicine, a general shift away from a narrow focus on religious doctrine, and a greater interest in spirituality, chaplaincy in institutions of both kinds will continue to have a significant role in the healing arts in the years to come.

Part 4

Attention to the social-cultural context

Different lyrics but the same tune
Multifaith spiritual care in a Canadian context

Patricia (Pam) Morrison Driedger

Many years ago a friend and I were engaged in a conversation about hospital chaplaincy. In the course of this conversation, he told me about a chaplain in a large hospital in Canada who was herself a practitioner of Wicca. At the time I wondered how such a person could be an effective chaplain. My comments, I am sorry to say, went something like this: "I rather doubt that there are enough practitioners of Wicca to keep a chaplain busy, and I think the differences between Wicca and most of the mainstream faiths are too great for a Wicca chaplain to be of much service to anyone else." I went on to say, "I am a fairly open-minded, multifaith oriented person, but I would be uncomfortable with the idea of someone who identified herself as a "white witch" offering me spiritual care. I would feel that this person's god was not my God, and I would wonder about what they were inviting into the conversation. If I feel that way, how would it be for someone from a "more conservative" background?

At the time of this conversation I thought that the role of hospital chaplain was to offer people the hope and the strength of faith during a difficult time. The chaplain would, I thought, speak the words of faith that would shore up a patient's lagging spirits and give him or her the courage to face whatever was coming. In my way of thinking, the effectiveness of the chaplain with any given patient would be somewhat dependent upon how closely aligned the chaplain's faith was to that of the patient. When I reflect upon my comments about the great distance between Wicca and more mainstream religions, I realize that I assumed that a Christian chaplain would be able to offer the best support to a person of their own denomination because they would know how to interpret and explain things in a way that fit with what the patient had been taught.

Pam Driedger, M.Div., recently completed serving as Director of Spiritual Care at Eden Mental Health Centre, Winkler, Manitoba, Canada.

The chaplain would be able to offer significant support to other Christians who held a large number of beliefs in common and some encouragement and insight to all who practice a monotheistic faith. I assumed a person from a pagan tradition would not be able to reflect any of my own beliefs back to me with enough conviction to make a difference. Even if she were able to recite the proper words, she wouldn't really know what they meant and so she wouldn't be of much support if my faith was at all shaky.

Today as I provide spiritual care for people from a wide variety of religious traditions, including earth-based traditions, and for people with no religious tradition whatsoever, I am somewhat embarrassed by my long-ago comments. Over the years I have learned to think differently not only about the role of a spiritual care provider in a multifaith setting, but also about what it means to have a multifaith orientation. I have come to believe that a multifaith outlook is not rooted in finding the common content or common beliefs in different religious traditions, but rather in recognizing the common process of faith and of orienting one's life around one's faith. While I used to think that the spiritual care provider had to share the specifics of a patient's faith, I now realize that the primary role of the spiritual care provider is to understand the way that faith permeates everything else in life and to engage patients from within the paradigm of faith.[1]

What is the Canadian context?

My thinking about what it means to provide spiritual care across religious traditions has been significantly influenced by the Canadian approach to diversity. Throughout Canadian society a high value is placed upon cultural diversity and cultural distinctiveness. Canadians regularly distinguish themselves from their neighbours in the United States by saying that Canada is a "mosaic" while the US is a "melting pot." One of the clearest examples of what this means is found in the Canadian approach to the national anthem.

Talk to any Olympic athlete who has won a gold medal and they will speak about the moment when they stood on the podium and their

---

[1] A paradigm is a philosophical and theoretical framework. There are many different paradigms which shape the day-to-day choices and the long term goals of individuals and communities. Not only individuals but also professions operate from within particular paradigms; within each profession practitioners observe, analyze and respond to the problems they encounter according to a specific set of criteria with a specific set of goals. When spiritual care providers interact with patients/clients their focus is on the meaning and value system which the care receivers have identified as their own. Spiritual care providers strive to understand and respond to issues of illness and health, hope and despair from the perspective of the patient/client rather than from some external, "objective" perspective.

national anthem began to play. Watch the faces of athletes when their national anthem is played at the opening of an international game. A national anthem is one of the central signs of communal identity and belonging. When an anthem is played it connects athletes to millions of people they have never met but who care about them and about what they will do. A national anthem is one of the central symbols and forces of unity.

Now consider Canada's national anthem.

"Oh Canada!
Our home and native land!
True patriot love in all thy sons command.
With glowing hearts
We see thee rise,
The true north, strong and free"

"Ô Canada! Terre de nos aïeux,
Ton front est ceint de fleurons glorieux!

Car ton bras sait porter l'épée,
Il sait porter la croix!

Ton histoire est une épopée
Des plus brillants exploits.

> "O Canada! Land of our forefathers
> Thy brow is wreathed with a glorious garland of flowers.
> As in thy arm ready to wield the sword,
> So also is it ready to carry the cross.
> Thy history is an epic of the most brilliant exploits."

"Uu Kanata!
Nangmini nunavut!
Piqujatii nalattiaqpavut."

> "Oh, Canada
> Snow falling from the sky. Snow on the ground.
> Snow dissolving into the sea. Snow building up on sea ice."

These are the opening stanzas of Canada's National Anthem as it is sung in English-speaking Canada, in French-speaking Canada, and in the territory of Nunavut: three distinct languages, three distinct meanings, but only one country, and only one tune. The music connects Canadians to one another and to their country even though different groups may have different understandings of what it means to be Canadian and what it means to be connected. The music influences the phrasing and sentence structure of the lyrics. It shapes the overall tone and atmosphere of the anthem and the way it is likely to touch and move the "soul," but the music does not influence the intellectual content. The music shapes the way the meaning will be heard and interpreted but it does not influence the basic meaning of the lyrics. The music links the hearts of people from different cultures without requiring that they link all of their thoughts.

The idea that the national anthem should be sung with different words in different places to reflect the distinct cultural perspectives and emphases of those places, rather than sung with one set of words which would highlight what all the cultures and regions hold in common, epitomizes the Canadian approach to diversity. This multicultural approach to the national anthem in Canada provides a window into understanding the multifaith approach to spiritual care in the Canadian context. Canadian spiritual care providers build upon the well-established tradition of playing a melody to which everyone can sing their own song even if everyone's lyrics are completely different.

Changing the thinking: Manitoba's experience

The recognition that it is a common melody (paradigm of faith) rather than common lyrics (the specific tenets of faith themselves) which creates a foundation for multifaith spiritual care did not spring up overnight. In Canada as in many other places, interfaith dialogue began with efforts to understand each other in a way that would allow for a de-emphasizing of differences and an emphasizing of commonalities. There was an effort to find an essential transcendent truth on which people of different faiths could agree. There was a sense that multifaith spirituality and multifaith care would find and attend to the common denominator in beliefs. It would not be ideal for anyone, but it would be better than nothing. Imagine everyone singing "O Canada ... ." (the first words of the Canadian anthem and the only words which all three languages share) and then humming the rest of the song.

In the past the importance of faith groups within the fabric of society was taken as a given. The primary threat to any particular religious group came from people who practiced religion in a different way. Faith communities worked together to improve their relationships with each other and to find the common denominator in their beliefs so that they would not use their influence to pull in opposite directions when in fact they shared a common goal.[2] In recent years the primary threat to faith communities has come from the secular community that sought to discredit or sideline all religious groups and concerns. Faith groups have begun working together not so much to find the commonalities in their beliefs but more to find the commonalities in their goals and in the paradigm out of which they operate. Now groups work together to help the secular world understand the place and value of faith and spirituality in the world, in whatever form they take.

The Province of Manitoba, where I live and work, has a very active interfaith community that has worked together for many years advocating for the importance of spiritual care for people in health care and correctional institutions. Initially, spiritual care was understood primarily as *pastoral* care and the primary concern of the Manitoba Interfaith Council[3] was that neither hospitalization nor incarceration be allowed to separate people from the supports of the faith community which might be instrumental in their recovery. In more recent years the Council has shifted its focus away from the shared interests of faith groups in caring for their own, to the shared belief of faith groups that the perspective of faith has a place in health care decisions and that attention to the concepts and constructs of faith affects health outcomes. While in the past the council advocated for the rights of faith groups to provide a type of care that is particularly appropriate for those of their tradition, today it advocates for the rights of patients to receive care that is attentive to their personal faith story whether that is in lock step with their inherited tradition, at odds with their tradition or somewhere in between. In the past the focus was on the rights of faith groups to practice their faith regardless of what others thought. Today the focus is on the spiritual nature of all people, those within and those outside of faith groups, and the importance of giving attention to that spiritual nature in any quest for health or rehabilitation.

One of the catalysts for this change in focus was the introduction of new privacy laws which raised questions about if and how spiritual caregivers could be informed of a person's hospital admission or condi-

---

[2] Consider the ecumenical movement which resulted in the formation of the World Council of Churches in the 1960s. Consider too the series of dialogues and subsequent accords between the Catholic Church and various other Christian denominations.

[3] The Manitoba Interfaith Council works to ensure the provision of spiritual care in provincial healthcare and correction institutions. MIC is particularly concerned that spiritual care be provided in a manner that honours the faith perspective of the client.

tion. There was concern that some of the prevailing interpretations of privacy laws would result in an artificial division between those providing spiritual care and those providing other forms of care to hospital patients and care home residents. This in turn might impair communication that might otherwise facilitate healing. Leaders from the various faith communities began by discussing their concerns that they would no longer be able to adequately serve those people who were on the fringes of their community, those whose health condition might be unknown to them, but who would need and want care at times of crisis.

As the discussions progressed, those involved became increasingly aware of the fact that although they might disagree about the specifics of faith, and the specifics regarding what it is that gives meaning and purpose to life, they all agreed that attention to the questions is essential to a person's well-being. They began to realize that their concern was not simply that people from their own tradition receive "religious care," but that all people receive a form of care that is attentive to the spirit. Conversations began to focus less on religious or faith needs and more on understanding the place of these needs in the overall understanding of health.

The Manitoba Interfaith Council, the Interfaith Health Care Association of Manitoba[4] and the Manitoba branch of the Canadian Association for Pastoral Practice and Education (CAPPE)[5] worked together and met many times with government to enhance the understanding of spiritual well being as an integral component of overall well-being. Much of the discussion was built around the modern understanding of health as more than just the absence of disease. The World Health Organization defines health as "a state of complete physical, mental and social well-being." The Manitoba Interfaith Council and the Interfaith Health Care Association of Manitoba and CAPPE stressed that both mental and social well-being depend upon a person's ability to find meaning and purpose in the midst of whatever is happening. Individuals are likely to be thrown into turmoil if they are unable to respond to the present circumstances within the meaning and decision-making framework which they have chosen for their lives. Physical or mental illness can result in significant spiritual distress and create a need for spiritual care. Spiritual care is intended to help people maintain or recover their sense of meaning and

---

[4] The Manitoba Interfaith Council has representatives from almost all of the faith groups which meet for worship in Manitoba. The Interfaith Healthcare Association of Manitoba's members include all of the healthcare organizations in the province which are owned and governed by faith groups. For more information on IHCAM see http://www.cham.mb.ca/IHCAM/index.

[5] For more information on CAPPE see www.cappe.org.

purpose when it is threatened or has been undermined by illness. When spiritual care is made available, health outcomes improve.

In 2004 health was officially defined in Manitoba law as "the condition of being sound in mind, body, and spirit."[6] The decision to make "sound in spirit" part of the definition of health reflected the consensus that an integral relationship exists between a person's spirituality and a person's response to illness and treatment plans. People inside and outside traditional faith structures wanted to ensure that in the pursuit of physical or mental health the impact of treatment on the patient's spiritual well-being was not overlooked. Furthermore, there was broad-based support for the concept of enabling patients to draw upon the strengths of their spiritual traditions to aid them in maximizing their well-being during illness and/or in the movement toward recovery.

Applying the Canadian approach to diversity to a clinical setting

The naming of spiritual well-being as a component of health resulted in the recognition of spiritual care as a distinct component of health care and not merely a service offered in support of "real" health care. This in turn has created a need to describe spiritual care outside of systems of faith, and to establish standards of spiritual care that can be understood within the context of the secular, without reference to any particular religious tradition or belief system. There is an increasing pressure to ensure that spiritual care is truly multifaith care, and that spiritual care providers are able to offer the highest standard of care to *all* people who have spiritual needs.

Spiritual caregivers in many places have learned to step outside of their own faith traditions in order to reach out to others who are in need or in pain and who are not being served by someone from their own tradition. In many settings, spiritual caregivers have learned to do this because of their own drive toward compassion. They have wanted to help and so have found a way to help. Multifaith care has been learned and is being learned by necessity more than by design. In Canada, the push toward multifaith care comes not just from individual care providers who see it as something which they must do out of compassion; the push comes even more strongly from the health care system itself. In order to understand the systemic drive toward multifaith spiritual care, it is necessary to reflect upon the Canadian approach to health care in general and the ongoing shift in the understanding of the place of spiritual care in health care.

The Canadian Health Care system is driven by a set of five principles

---

[6] Bill 43, 2nd Session, 38th Legislature, The Personal Health Information Amendment Act.

which impact every aspect of health care. These five principles are: public administration, comprehensiveness, universality, portability and accessibility.[7] All five of these principles influence Canadian thinking around spiritual care.

Because health is publicly administered, decisions with respect to the place of spiritual care within the health system are open to public discussion and debate and policy. In the past, pastoral care was primarily viewed as something which various faith groups offered to patients in hospitals and residents in care homes. Pastoral care was something that patients carried from their home lives to the hospital or care home; it was not an integral part of the health care plan. Pastoral care was most commonly found in facilities which were owned and governed by faith communities. This was because these communities established health care facilities as a means of ensuring that illness would not isolate a person from community supports, and pastoral care was recognized as one of the important community supports. From a public policy perspective, pastoral care was seen as one of the things which a caring community had the right to offer as a part of their self-expression. If a community chose to offer pastoral care, they had the right to do so as long as such care was not imposed on those who did not want it, or made a condition for the reception of other care.

In recent years, there has been a mounting body of evidence measuring the positive impact of spiritual care on health outcomes.[8] As health care decision-makers reflected upon this evidence they began to think of spiritual care not as something that the community brings into the hospital but as something the hospital offers the community. As soon as spiritual care became a service of the hospital to the community and not the other way around, it became necessary to apply the principles of comprehensiveness, universality, and accessibility. This in turn led to a shift in the way spiritual care is understood and offered.

If Canada's health care system were driven primarily by market forces, spiritual care would be provided when those who were paying indicated a strong desire for the care or when the hospital administration believed that spiritual care had a positive effect on the bottom line. In a market driven system, the hospital must make sure that it does not interfere with a patient's right to receive spiritual care from those who choose

---

[7] See The Canada Health Act: Overview and Options: www.parl.gc.ca/information/library.

[8] See Levin J. *God, Faith and Health: Exploring the Spirituality-Healing Connection*. New York, NY: John Wiley and Sons; 2001. See also Culliford, Larry, "Spiritual care and psychiatric treatment: an introduction," *Advances in Psychiatric Treatment* (2002) 8: 249-258, The Royal College of Psychiatrists.

to make it available, but the hospital does not have a responsibility for providing that care for any given faith group unless that group's market share dictates such a responsibility. Canada's health care system, however, is not primarily driven by market forces (although it is influenced by them); it is driven by principles. And these principles necessitate that a change in the understanding of the impact of spiritual care will require a change in the way spiritual care is provided. This is because a change in the understanding of the impact of spiritual care creates a change in the responsibilities resting with the care provider.

Based on the principles of comprehensiveness, universality, and accessibility, if spiritual care has been demonstrated to have a significant positive and cost effective effect on health outcomes, it should be included in the service provided to all patients. It is not sufficient to say that the majority of patients in this organization are Catholic or Protestant therefore we will have Catholic and Protestant chaplains who will serve people in their respective groups and provide for others "to the extent that they are able." Nor is it sufficient to say that pastoral caregivers from Jewish, Christian, and Protestant communities are willing to come and offer services, but there is no one from the Islamic community so we will be unable to offer spiritual care to Moslems. In keeping with the Canadian philosophy of care, if the organization is going to provide spiritual care for some patients it has a responsibility to provide comparable care for every patient, even those who come from very small minorities. Since it is not possible to provide a chaplain for every religious group or every type of spirituality that is represented among hospital patients, it has become necessary to think about spiritual care in new ways.

This change in thinking can be seen in a change in language from speaking about *pastoral* care in clinical settings to speaking about *spiritual* care. The words, "pastor" and "pastoral" conjure up images of a shepherd with a flock. The shepherd guides the flock from where they are to a better place, carefully skirting dangers and pulling those who would wander back from precipices or out of ditches. The flock follows because they know the shepherd's voice and have learned to trust it. Within a faith context, the pastor shepherds the flock on its journey toward God or toward ultimate reality, and helps individuals find the things which will nourish them on the journey and avoid the things which will harm them. The flock follows because they recognize the pastor's voice, words, and tone. Any who are not comfortable with the voice, words, and tone will not follow. They will know that they must wait for another shepherd—a different pastor.

The presumption in the shift of language from "pastoral care" to "spiritual care" is that even if no pastor arrives to lead a person, it is possible to support their spiritual journey in a way that fosters health. Looking at the various studies around spiritual care, it would appear that it is not the end goal of a particular spiritual path that is the primary determinant of health, but rather the process of spiritual discernment. To return to the opening musical analogy, it is not the lyrics but the melody which makes the song of the spirit what it is.

Becoming a spiritual caregiver instead of a pastor

The traditional role of the pastor is to lead the spiritual song; as with the national anthem of Canada, the meaning of the song will depend upon the language (in this case the spiritual language) which the leader knows and chooses. It is difficult to imagine a Christian pastor knowing and choosing a spiritual song that did not call people into relationship with the God revealed in Jesus. A Buddhist would be inclined to choose a song that encouraged the patient to let go of their strong sense of "self" and their belief that there is anyone or anything that is truly "other." The Native American song would emphasize the permanent connectedness of all things and the influence of each upon the others. It would be difficult, if not impossible, to lead people and serve as pastor for people from very different traditions without losing one's own authenticity. It would be difficult if not impossible to sing one song that would have deep meaning for people from all three of these traditions, but it would be possible to play a melody that was recognizable and significant within each tradition.

The shared melody of all spiritual traditions is heard in the questions of meaning and purpose that are the same for everyone.[9] The music of the spirit is expressed in the universal quest for love, inner peace, belonging, and hope. This quest is the same whether one is Christian or Muslim, Jewish or Buddhist or agnostic. All people have a need to ask questions about the meaning, purpose, and value of life; and each person needs to find answers that enable him or her to respond to the unique experiences of his or her own life. Some people will be conscious of the fact that they have asked and answered these questions. Others will be content with the answers provided to them by their families and communities and may be unaware that there are questions to be asked. Nevertheless the questions and the answers still exist and create the framework for each person's existence, and the basis for every decision. The role of the spiritual caregiver is to recognize the importance of the spiritual process

---

[9] The spiritual nature of human beings can be understood from an anthropological perspective as well as from a theological perspective. A widely cited definition of spirituality which refers to these common questions can be found in Murray, R.B. and Zentner, J.P. , *Nursing Concepts for Health Promotion*, (London: Prentice Hall, 1989), p. 259.

in shaping every aspect of life and to provide accompaniment for people as they engage in the process.

The role of a spiritual care provider in a multifaith health care environment is not to help people find a particular set of answers to their questions, but instead to help them become more aware of the ways in which their own framework of questions and answers impacts their health and their health-related choices. The spiritual care provider is also expected to be attentive to the impact and/or significance of decisions made by the treatment team when viewed through the patient's particular worldview or lens of faith. When necessary the spiritual caregiver can help present treatment decisions in a manner that makes sense within the context of the patient's faith, and/or present the patient's faith concerns in a manner that makes sense within the paradigms used by the treatment team.

Each member of the treatment team within a health care facility has a particular expertise and a particular perspective from which he or she views the well-being of patients and advocates for a transformation from illness to wellness. The spiritual caregiver is the member of the treatment team whose expertise is the realm of faith and spirituality. The significant tasks of the spiritual caregiver in a multifaith environment include: 1) understanding how individual belief systems and communal belief systems impact a person's health and a person's response to treatment; 2) entering into the faith paradigm of the patient, as it is presented by the patient, in order to hear the cry of the spirit; 3) being a listening presence accompanying the patient through illness from within their own worldview/understanding of illness; 4) enabling the patient to use the resources which he or she can see in his or her own faith as sources of strength, hope, meaning and purpose; 5) helping the health care team recognize the conflicts that arise because the faith paradigms of the team and the faith paradigms of the patient are not the same and 6) helping the patient and the care team to address any conflicts which exist between the patient's spiritual goals and the patient's other health goals.

Providing multifaith care as a Christian caregiver

In the normal course of events, individuals choose their own paradigm of belief, find their own sense of meaning and purpose, and walk their own spiritual path. Some walk that path in the company of a faith community, following the map of an established religious tradition. Others develop a meaning system that is uniquely their own, drawing on inputs from a variety of religious, philosophical, and secular sources. Traditional Christian teaching holds that any path that is not directed toward the One God, who became human in the person of Jesus and remains in the world through the presence of the Holy Spirit, is a dead end. Different Christian denominations have different understandings of what it means to walk a path oriented toward God, but all accept the individual's right to choose his or her own path.

This acceptance of the right of individuals to choose their own spiritual path can become more complicated during periods of significant illness. This is because significant illness often throws people off their chosen paths or brings to light significant hazards along those paths. When any of us see other people who are finding it difficult to follow the path which they have chosen, it can be very tempting for us to encourage them to try a new path. Many Christians watching non-Christians struggle with feelings such as hopelessness, despair, doubt, anxiety or guilt, honestly believe that if the non-Christian would come to know Christ, his or her journey would not be as hard. It can be tempting for the Christian spiritual caregiver to suggest Christian faith as the support that will make a difference to a patient who is struggling. This temptation is not unique to spiritual caregivers. It can also be tempting for a Christian doctor, a Christian nurse or a Christian social worker to suggest their faith as a part of the best treatment plan. Like the others, spiritual caregivers need to remember that their task is not to evangelize but to offer health care, and in fact using their position of power as a health care provider to evangelize would be wrong.

Doctors, nurses, and social workers often avoid the temptation of imposing their faith on patients and clients by avoiding spiritual issues altogether. Spiritual caregivers cannot do that; instead they have to hone their skills in enabling the spiritual process without prescribing the spiritual content. The multifaith nature of our health care facilities is forcing spiritual care providers and others to recognize that spiritual health care is not about providing a set of answers but about helping people identify and wrestle with a set of questions.

Jesus said, "Ask, and it will be given to you; seek, and you will find; knock, and the door will be opened." (Matthew 7:7) The Christian spiritual caregiver, the Jewish spiritual caregiver and the Wiccan spiritual caregiver all can help patients ask, seek, and knock. It is important that the caregiver be rooted in his or her own faith tradition because that rootedness enables the caregiver to truly understand the significance of the spiritual process. As with any health care practitioner, the specific faith of the caregiver may motivate the caregiver and may give meaning and purpose to his or her work, but the terms of the caregiver's faith are not the focus of a spiritual care visit. This is because the spiritual caregiver plays the melody, but the care receiver provides the words.

Competencies for pastoral work in multicultural and multifaith societies

Anke Flohr

In my many years of ministry away from my mother church, the Northelbian Evangelical Lutheran Church, I have discovered that the academic training and encouragement I received provided a solid base for my work.[1] To my surprise I found out that my upbringing as a farm girl—born and raised in a small farming community fifty kilometers east of Hamburg—became more and more an asset. In my early years on the farm, I learned something about the importance and interdependence of community with each other and with the land. I had to travel to the other side of the world to appreciate the simple truth of the importance of family and community and the value of nurturing relationships with people and nature. My Samoan friends say it boldly: "Family is our life insurance." Coming from North-European, Protestant roots I have always put individualism and independence as my top guidelines. The rediscovery of the simple truth of the importance of interdependent communities has been a major learning, or shall I say "relearning," for me in the last decade. I am therefore also grateful to my parents and family for having given me a firm foundation for my life; it is a foundation that sustains the professional work partially reflected in the following pages.

Anke Flohr, M.Div., an ordained minister in the Evangelical Lutheran Church in America, was a supervisor and Director of Clinical Pastoral Education at Pacific Health Ministry, Honolulu, Hawaii. She was also a board certified chaplain serving at the Good Samaritan Retirement Community at Pohai Nani, Kaneohe. Currently she is the Professional Leader/Education Supervisor at Sunnybrook Health Sciences Centre, Toronto, Ontario, Canada.

[1] My special thanks goes to Professor Theo Ahrens. It was my honor to have studied under him at the Institute for Missiology, Ecumenics and Religious Studies (Department of Protestant Theology at the University of Hamburg). It was Professor Ahrens, in the early eighties, who opened the doors for me to embrace cultural diversity and follow my calling to specialize in research, pastoral care and counseling in multicultural societies, especially the communities in the region of Oceania, such as in Papua New Guinea.

In the first part of this essay—"Context, challenge, and guidelines"—I will introduce the context, "Hawaii," from which I speak and I will describe the need for new competencies for pastoral work in multicultural and multifaith communities. I will explore seven areas of competency: passion, personal awareness, knowledge, skills, action, embracing ambiguity and patience. In summary I use Pacific Health Ministry as an example of how to teach multicultural competencies in pastoral care. In the second part—"A window to reflective practice"—I will present an interfaith care situation including verbatim material and a comprehensive analysis.

Part 1
Context, challenge, and guidelines

Context: Pacific Health Ministry in Hawaii

I joined Pacific Health Ministry[2] in Hawaii in 1994 to specialize in Clinical Pastoral Education (CPE) and to become a CPE supervisor. The pastoral care agency then was eight years old, founded and sponsored by local churches, temples, and communities of all faiths expressing a need for spiritual care in the major hospitals of the island of Oahu.[3] Pacific Health Ministry (then called Interfaith Ministries of Hawaii) was asked to provide spiritual care and education for a community that had become a "mosaic" of about fifty diverse (immigrant) cultures and traditions in the last two hundred years. The first immigrants were the Hawaiian people themselves (700–900 CE). The Native Hawaiians established their monarchy with about 300,000 people. They had a single, understood lifestyle, religion, and culture. Change came with the arrival of James Cook from England in 1778.

American and European businessmen were followed by three large waves of immigrants from China, Japan, and the Philippines until the early 1900s. Smaller immigrant groups came from Korea, Portugal, and a few other European countries. The need for cheap, compliant agricultural workers was great on the many sugar plantations. American missionaries (Congregationalists) from New England arrived in 1820. The State of Hawaii Data Book 2004[4] estimates that about 33 percent of the current population is European/American, 23 percent Japanese, 19 percent Filipino, nine percent Native Hawaiian, six percent Chinese and other

---

[2] http://www.pacifichealthministry.org

[3] Hawaii consists of eight islands with a population of about 1,275,000. Eighty per cent of all people live on the island of Oahu It's capitol is Honolulu.

[4] http://hawaii.gov/dbedt/info/economic/databook/

mainly Asian and Pacific Island groups. The widely accepted practice of intermarriage has left many individuals with complex ethnic backgrounds. For example, it is very common for a person to say, "I am Hawaiian, Chinese, German, and Korean." People in Hawaii often define their identity as a "local identity" which consists of their own ethnic roots blended together in Hawaii to a rather unique lifestyle which expresses its love for diversity and living on the islands. Living the "Aloha Spirit" is one expression of that. The Native Hawaiians claim their Hawaiian identity and resent the overthrow of their last Queen, Queen Liliuokalani, in 1893, and the fact that Hawaii became the 50th state of the US in 1959. There are constant tensions between those who embrace the new "local identity/local culture" and those who want the sovereignty and their "aina" (land) back which was lost to more recent immigrant people.

Hawaii has many cultures and ethnic groups living closely together with as many languages spoken as there are different ethnic groups. Each group has brought its culture and religion with them. Each has developed unique ways of understanding life and death. Each practices healing and gives care to people in special ways. In Hawaii approximately 50 percent of the population is Christian with more than two dozen denominations. These include the Roman Catholic Church, which is the largest, the Southern Baptist, United Methodist, Episcopalian, United Church of Christ, the Church of Jesus Christ of Latter-Day Saints and, in the last 10 years, several fast-growing Foursquare churches. Buddhists comprise 35 percent with seven major sects. The Honpa Hongwanji is the largest and most influential group. The rest is a combination of Jewish, Islamic, and native Hawaiian beliefs, and other religions and people who have no particular religious affiliation. Many people living in Hawaii would say that they are "spiritual" and that their "local culture" has a lot to do with their spirituality. Learning to minister to all people as they face a crisis in life is a central focus of Clinical Pastoral Education. In Hawaii being able to engage in "interfaith dialogue" is a necessity for chaplains which creates interesting learning opportunities: "Can I fully serve others who are different from me?"

In the ten major hospitals and health care facilities on Oahu in which Pacific Health Ministry chaplains serve, we encounter patients, families, and staff from all backgrounds. Chaplains with Pacific Health Ministry make well over sixty thousand pastoral contacts a year. The essence of the mission of Pacific Health Ministry is to be Kukulu Kumuhana. "Kukulu Kumuhana" has a special significance in the Hawaiian culture. It is the process of "pooling together" in unity the spiritual, emotional, and psychological strengths of the individual who is ill or in a special circumstance with that of family, friends, and other concerned individuals to achieve a positive outcome.

A more commonly used clinical word for "pooling together" is the word *assessing*: To be a professional spiritual care provider in this multicultural and multifaith setting we need to be competent in assessing those we serve and "pooling together" information and people. We always seek to look at the *whole person*—mind/body/spirit—in her or his context and are concerned with how a person finds meaning and purpose in life, including a sense of belonging and connectedness. We gather insight about their lives considering spiritual, psycho-social/interpersonal, emotional, intellectual, vocational, ethnic/racial/cultural and physical dimensions. Following that data, the health care chaplains develop care plans together with the interdisciplinary care team. This assessment process, the "Kukulu Kumuhana" is supported by a *ministry of presence*, which builds relationship by creating a non-judgmental environment of compassion and care. The spiritual care provider comes from a place of humility in conjunction with the ability to think critically. Pamela A. Hays says it well: "People with genuine humility are effective helpers, because they are realistic about what they have to offer, aware of their own limitations and accepting of the contribution of others."[5]

The need for multicultural and multifaith competencies in pastoral work

Hawaii is unique because it is culturally so diverse and so isolated by the Pacific Ocean. By most peoples' descriptions, Hawaii is called "Paradise." It truly is a "Paradise" for multicultural learning and teaching and offers its "manao" (knowledge) to the world. Beyond, Hawaii's cultural diversity is part of the fabric of North American social life. One third of the U.S. population comes from other cultural traditions than the still predominant European-American. By the year 2050 this number is estimated to have increased to more than 50 percent of the US population. Over 2,000 identifiable expressions of religion and spiritual paths were found in the USA.[6] We are involved in a multicultural and multifaith revolution. We live in a world that has many points of view about what "reality" is. Mary A Fukuyama and Todd D. Sevig define multiculturalism as "many cultures, many worldviews, many languages, many values, and many

---

[5] Pamela A. Hays. *Addressing Cultural Complexities in Practice* (Washington, D.C.: American Psychological Association, 2004), p. 25.

[6] J. Creedon. "God with a Million Faces," *Utne Reader* (July–August 1998), 42–48.

customs, existing and serving to form human communities. Secondly, it means seeking common ground, respecting differences, and working for social justice in a system that historically has kept various groups from access to resources and power."[7] This means that "multiculturalism" is more than a descriptor of a social situation; it also denotes certain values. In a multicultural society, cross-cultural and intercultural engagements are the norm.

The new context of our times is a globalized community with international relations. The complexity of our multicultural and globalized world with its new spiritual demands is challenging for pastoral/spiritual care providers. Multicultural competencies are now required for chaplains in U.S. and Canadian hospitals. My Korean American colleague Samuel Lee from the Claremont School of Theology—who was raised in Hawaii—compares the multicultural interactions in pastoral care with the movements of dance partners.[8] For three years we served together on the Multicultural Taskforce of the Association for Clinical Pastoral Education. In those years the task force members tried to learn together "multicultural dance steps" to become multicultural dancers who open up to meaningful encounters across and beyond differences in order to be mutually enriched and transformed by meeting the other. Having attempted to learn the Hula after moving to Hawaii, I understand Lee's dance metaphor and all the discipline, practice, good attitude, resiliency, physical strength and endurance it takes before the dance with the group starts becoming harmonious.

Seven multicultural-multifaith dance steps

To the question of what makes a competent pastoral/spiritual care provider in our multicultural and multifaith society, therefore, we respond with a choreography including the following steps.

Passion

Passion is the first essential competency. It is energy, curiosity, a calling for the process and often the hard work of encountering the unknown, engaging "otherness" and leaving one's comfort zone. It is the ability to

[7] Mary A. Fukuyama and Todd D. Sevig. "Cultural Diversity in Pastoral Care," in Robert G. Anderson and Mary A. Fukuyama, eds. *Ministry in the Spiritual and Cultural Diversity of Health Care* (New York: The Haworth Pastoral Press, 2004), p. 28.

[8] K. Samuel Lee. "Becoming Multicultural Dancers: The Pastoral Practitioner in a Multicultural Society." *Journal of Pastoral Care*, 33 (2001), 389–396. For the use of the dance metaphor in pastoral theology, see also Luis Elier Rodríguez, "Intercultural Awareness in Spiritual Caregiving: An Invitation to Dance with God," in Leah Dawn Bueckert and Daniel S. Schipani, eds., *Spiritual Caregiving in the Hospital: Windows to Chaplaincy Ministry* (Kitchener: Pandora Press, 2006), p. 93–104.

deeply care for multicultural encounters and to articulate this care to others.[9] It is the ability to connect head and heart, express compassion and truly value difference and unfamiliar territory. It means taking risks, making oneself vulnerable, unlearning and learning. It goes far beyond the initial excitement, interest or thrill in "different faces, accents, foods, and ways of looking at life."[10] Without a passion for these types of encounters, little will be learned.

Personal awareness

Self awareness as cultural beings and an understanding of one's own personal and cultural values and beliefs is an important second step in becoming more competent as pastoral and spiritual caregivers. The ability to know and explain one's own spiritual and cultural background is crucial.[11] To examine one's cultural background the Pacific Health Ministry CPE team found the ADDRESSING model of cultural assessment developed by our colleague Pamela Hays from Anchorage, Alaska, especially helpful.[12] We apply it with the staff and Clinical Pastoral Education students. ADDRESSING is an acronym that identifies a framework for understanding the personal and cultural development of individuals. Each letter represents a word that is a component of one's life and experience:

A   stands for age and generational influences (describing my generation, how it has shaped me and continues to shape me in accordance to or in rebellion to it)

D   stands for developmental (my experiences of growth and maturation)

D   stands for acquired disabilities (my physical condition and my relation with my body seen through the lens of my culture)

R   stands for religion and spiritual orientation (my relationship with the Transcendent, as well as my inner self and neighbor, seen through received teachings, cultural influences and personal experiences)

E   stands for ethnicity (common ancestry through which I have evolved shared values and customs)

---

[9] A. Cavina, "Multicultural Competencies in Clinical Pastoral Education: Clinical Issues in Cultural Competencies." Unpublished presentation at the annual ACPE conference, Portland, Oregon, October 2004.

[10] A. M. Van Beek, *Cross-Cultural Counseling* (Minneapolis: Fortress Press, 1996), p. 101.

[11] Robert G. Anderson, "The Search for Spiritual/Cultural Competency in Chaplaincy Practice: Five Steps that Mark the Path," in Anderson and Fukuyama, Ministry in the Spiritual and Cultural Diversity of Health Care, p. 13.

[12] Hays, *Addressing Cultural Complexities in Practice*.

S   stands for socio-economic status (the influence of class and economy in my development as an individual)

S   stands for sexual orientation (how it has been influenced by my own culture of origin; how it has shaped my relationship with my cultural groups, and with others and their worldviews)

I   stands for indigenous heritage (cultural heritage within my ethnicity)

N   stands for national origin (my political status and citizenship)

G   stands for gender (the constructed gender identity that I received and my gender identity development).

As the reader can see, with each letter Pamela Hays signifies assessment of the impact of power or the lack of it for people. The awareness of cultural privilege, unearned advantages, unintentional racism, assumptions, and biases can come to the forefront. Experiences of being discriminated against by age, disability, ethnicity, socio-economic status and gender orientation can be named. In using the ADDRESSING model as a personal cultural history framework one will hopefully recognize that one's own cultural heritage "did not constitute the world, but a world, and that embracing cultural diversity would both expand and destabilize a person's understanding of his or her world."[13]

The ADDRESSING model has become my preferred tool in working with Clinical Pastoral Education participants. I invite people to write about each letter and then share with the CPE group what they choose. A Hawaiian student told me that this method allowed her to share her "na'au." The "na'au" are literally the intestines but in Hawaiian understanding the seat of speaking one's heart and mind. The ADDRESSING model allowed her to speak of her pain in searching for her identity as a Hawaiian woman; she suggested that we always look for the "na'au" when inquiring about a person's culture. Her Korean peer was not familiar with the "na'au" but with "han." "Han" is the Korean concept of psychological and spiritual hurt caused by unjust oppression and suffering. "Han" Is central to the Korean cultural and personal identity. Like "na'au" it forms people's self awareness. The self-knowledge that comes with such learning as described above is essential to understanding the dynamics in cross-cultural pastoral relationships with the clients we serve.

Knowledge and training

Once engaged in this ongoing self-assessment process, the third step

---

[13] T. Breisford & C.R. Foster, *We are the Church Together: Cultural Diversity in Congregational Life* (Valley Forge: Trinity Press International, 1996), p. 11.

for pastoral/spiritual caregivers is to learn about diverse identities. This step addresses the ability to be sensitive, to identify and to learn from experience and about information that is outside of one's own cultural reference. The pastoral/spiritual care provider needs to have multicultural knowledge and training and needs to continue to expand and develop specialized knowledge about history, traditions, faith practices, lifestyle, and family systems—in short the worldviews of various ethnic groups and cultures. This includes familiarity with cultural identity development theories and conceptual frameworks. The ADDRESSING model used for assessment of others may help as a source of information. The care provider needs to be knowledgeable about issues around identity, power (history of dominance and oppression), social location, and connection/isolation. Other areas of knowledge are the use of time and space, the relation of individual and community, the focus on content or context, values, and beliefs connected to life and death and life cycle, and distinctions between sacred and profane, personal and public.[14]

This learning process is not always a clear-cut book learning and gathering of facts, but rather a process that pushes the learner beyond her/his comfort zone. Also, diversity brings multiple perspectives, and multiple perspectives often lead to conflict. For example, a CPE student from Mexico explained the traditional role men have in his culture. He often said "it is a guy thing," such as hanging out with other men and joking together. One of his female North American peers in the group who was raised in California was offended by his joking, laughing, and his assumed—as she called it—"sense of entitlement." She found disrespectful what he found totally "normal." Both explained their cultural reasons. And both did not like what they learned about each other. Yet, they continued to dialogue and found a "meeting place/space of exchange" in this process. "The between" became an essential dimension in the meeting of these two students without reinforcing *dominant power structures but rather by showing respect for each other.*

Skills

The saying attributed to Abraham Maslow puts it well, "If the only tool you have is a hammer, everything looks like a nail." The task for chaplains working in a multicultural environment is to gain a broad spectrum of skills that will help them to encounter the culturally different client and establish effective communication and connection across cultures. The

---

[14] Derald Wing Sue and David Sue, *Counseling the Culturally Diverse: Theory and Practice*, 5th ed. (Hoboken: John Wiley & Sons, 2007), Section I, "The Multiple Dimensions of Multicultural Counseling and Therapy," pp. 1–311.

qualities of a culturally competent pastoral/spiritual care provider reflect cultural humility, an acceptance of and openness to differences among people, genuineness, warmth, and empathy. To provide accurate empathy, the spiritual care provider needs to enter the "cultural borderland,"[15] the area where differences and similarities overlap and then develop a tolerance for ambiguity and create a space for not knowing. Further, the pastoral care provider needs to have good communication skills. They must be attending and responding; they must have language skills; they must be able to receive both verbal and nonverbal messages in response to direct and non-direct communication styles; they must pay attention to body language, voice, emotional expressions, and relational dynamics. And, they must be able to establish a connection across differences. When faced with barriers and limitations—both situational and interpersonal— the spiritual care provider needs to be able to access resources to assist her/him and make appropriate referrals.

A CPE student from Myanmar used to sit in our CPE classes with crossed arms resting on his upper body. My "quick judgment" was that he was probably not really interested, sleepy or somehow protective. Being aware of the danger of "quick judgments" in multicultural work I clarified my assumption with him. I learned that in his culture this body posture shows respect for the teacher and peers and shows full attention.

Action

Step five describes the ability to behave or act in a manner consistent with the above steps. It brings together passion, awareness, knowledge, and skills and goes into action.[16] It asks pastoral care providers to be watchful of their pastoral practice, to be faithful to the many lived realities and, in the words of Samuel Lee, to "keep the dance floor open for all persons."[17] They are asked to look at the larger picture and larger issues in the community, to reflect a global consciousness and to invite transformation and change. Pastoral caregivers need to be able to move beyond individual dialogue to broader actions and community involvement. The practice being called for is a constant process of working on a personal, institutional, and systemic level. For example, in hospitals chaplains are involved in Ethics Committees, Palliative Care Committees, End-of-Life support and other groups that attempt to improve patient care and monitor the health care system. Chaplains usually have teaching responsibilities in

[15] Cavina, "Multicultural Competencies in Clinical Pastoral Education."

[16] Mary A. Fukuyama and Todd D. Sevig, *Integrating Spirituality into Multicultural Counseling* (Thousand Oaks: Sage Publications, 1999), p. 71.

[17] Lee, "Becoming Multicultural Dancers," p. 386.

the broader health care system.

Pacific Health Ministry (PHM) began six years ago to expand its services from the hospitals to low-income housing areas and areas where the many homeless live. PHM nurses offer free basic health check-ups and consultation. PHM chaplains accompany them and offer spiritual support. Together with other community groups and churches they try to make a difference in the lives of people who are least supported and most marginalized in Hawaii.

Embracing ambiguity

I mentioned this step earlier as part of the needed skill-building. Learning to live with ambiguity is a key step. The pastoral and spiritual work in multicultural communities is not a place for experts. Working in pastoral care means learning to live in a dilemma and in a "grey zone." The multicultural pastoral care provider is asked to embrace a "both/and" perspective and, for instance, to be able to say with integrity, "I can be a Christian and value someone else's experience and faith." What the multiculturally-skilled chaplain knows to do is to be in a constant interfaith/intercultural dialogue—a two-way street of meeting each other. There is not just one truth in pastoral/spiritual work in multicultural communities. The All Believers Network Hawaii under the co-leadership of Sr. Joan Chatfield—one of the founding members of Pacific Health Ministry—held an island-wide conference in the fall of 2006 on the theme: "Moving from Exclusion to Inclusion in My Faith." A similar conference was held the year before and it caused tensions for some Clinical Pastoral Education students who wanted to speak their faith and proselytize. To learn to live with these tensions is part of the sixth dance step. Diana Eck says it this way, "The diversity of communities, traditions, understandings of truth, and visions of God is not an obstacle for us to overcome, but an opportunity for our energetic engagement and dialogue with one another. It does not mean giving up our commitments but rather opening up those commitments to the give-and-take of mutual discovery, understanding, and indeed, transformation."[18] In my own personal life I realized that the many years of sharing meeting places with people from other cultures and religions led me to a deepening of my own faith.

Patience

Living and working in a multicultural world takes a lot of patience. The "dance steps" mentioned earlier require lots of practice and constant

---

[18] Diana Eck, *Encountering God: A Spiritual Journey from Bozeman to Banaras*. (Boston: Beacon Press, 1993), p. 168.

learning and reflection.

Two years ago a group of about one hundred Lutheran women from various Lutheran parishes in California came to Hawaii to hold a conference about women in the Lutheran church. This felt so easy for me, a refreshing breather because we all claimed Lutheran roots, were all women (mainly of Scandinavian/German descent) with similar goals, wanted to be change-agents for justice, peace, and integrity of creation, and prayed and worshipped in the same ways. In all these years in Hawaii I had almost forgotten how easy it is to be in a group of people who are more similar to me than different.

There is comfort in being alike, feeling a sense of belonging, participating in family and group rituals, and speaking a particular language. I think it is much easier to "dance" with German Lutherans than in a Hawaiian Hula Halau (dance group) or on the multicultural dance floor. But with enough patience and deep breath the new steps can be learned.

Teaching and learning multicultural competencies

The most effective way to grow professionally as intercultural and interfaith caregivers is by exposure and direct experience. The CPE environment, its experiential form of education, and its "action-reflection-action" model deal with—as the founding father Anton Boisen said—"living human documents."[19] This process learning allows the CPE participant to reflect on cultural encounters as they happen. Learning emerges out of pastoral encounters. CPE by nature creates meeting spaces; they are spaces of exchange where trust grows through relationships. CPE with Pacific Health Ministry is like a multicultural interactive laboratory. Not only do the patients, families, and hospital staff come from diverse ethnic backgrounds, but so also does the CPE group itself. We purposefully bring together chaplaincy students from a variety of countries with different ethnic, cultural, and faith backgrounds. At the time of this writing, the group has students from Indonesia, the Philippines, Korea, Hawaii, and North-America. The facilitators and teaching chaplains are equally diverse. I am German, and others have Japanese, Chinese, Indian, Filipino, African American, and other North American cultural roots. The guest speakers represent a variety of community leaders from different faith traditions as well. Excursions to and immersion into Hawaii's diverse faith groups are part of the CPE curriculum.

On the CPE journey of discovery the participants leave their comfort zones. In the CPE group everyone is a teacher and everyone is a student.

---

[19] See Anton Boisen's essay, "Clinical training in theological education: The period of beginnings." *Chicago Theological Seminary Register* (1953).

Much time is spent with understanding each other and the meaning behind the words spoken and unspoken—many CPE participants do this in their second language which often brings major challenges, especially when it comes to the use of humor and idioms.

The group reality cannot be defined by one set of cultural assumptions; there is no right way. The participants step away from their assumptions and see other ways of looking at questions and issues. We also look at the simultaneous conversations that are going on at any time, the external verbal exchanges and the many other internal dialogues in people's heads.

Sometimes students—probably many of us once in a while—"hide" behind their culture. For example a student from Puerto Rico had issues with professional boundaries when visiting patients. He spent an enormous amount of time with each patient and their loved ones and got overinvolved. He explained that in his cultural understanding a pastoral visitation meant limitless care and concern for those who suffer. He did not see that his own needs and neediness were leading him in his work as chaplain. Culture in this case was used as an "excuse" to not change and learn. Sometimes when I am tired I get impatient. Then, I can get very directive, want things done right away, my way and I express it clearly. In those times I am lucky that I have good colleagues who check with me: "What's the matter with you?," they ask. Then I hear myself saying, "I am German. I like things done a certain way. I can't help it." The truth is, I can help it, of course, and so can anyone else. But it requires intentional effort to stay in dialogue as spiritual and cultural beings so as to dismantle the walls against others and one's personal and professional growth. Unfortunately, there are many cultural, religious, and other walls in our world. My hope is that conferences and books like this and the widespread multicultural movement will inspire many to become multicultural and multifaith dancers.

In the CPE environment, by design, the participants are encouraged to take dance steps. Stepping on each other's toes is part of the experience. In the CPE laboratory we learn how to embrace the complexity of multiculturally lived realities and how to be the best pastoral caregiver we can be, equipped with helpful multicultural and interfaith skills and knowledge.[20]

---

[20] At the conclusion of CPE Level II (ACPE *Standards Manual* [2005], pp. 12–13) students are able to:

Pastoral Formation

312.1 articulate an understanding of the pastoral role that is congruent with their personal values,

Part 2
A window to reflective practice

Introduction and verbatim

Ms. N. is a 94-year-old female Japanese American living in a nursing home. I have known her since she moved to the nursing home eight years ago. Due to strokes her speech is very slow and reduced to words and short sentences. She speaks English and Japanese. The charge nurse asked me to see Ms. N. because she was "upset because she experienced spirits in her room." I found Ms. N. in the dining room at her table, much earlier than lunch time. Her table mates had not arrived yet. I asked her whether I could sit down with her. She smiled and invited me to sit down. The visit lasted 40 minutes.

C = Chaplain

N = Ms. N.

Italic ( ) = Chaplain's feelings, thoughts, internal conversation

Non-italic ( ) = description of what is happening

C1 (sitting at the table) "Good morning, Ms. N. I am glad to see you today. How are you feeling today? *(I always enjoy visiting with Ms. N. I have warm and caring feelings for her.)*

N1 Not so good. (She stops smiling.)

C2 (soft spoken) Oh. (silent moment) I am sorry to hear that you are not feeling so good today.

---

basic assumptions and personhood.

Pastoral Competence

312.2 provide pastoral ministry to diverse people, taking into consideration multiple elements of cultural and ethnic differences, social conditions, systems, and justice issues without imposing their own perspectives.

312.3 demonstrate a range of pastoral skills, including listening/attending, empathic reflection, conflict resolution/confrontation, crisis management, and appropriate use of religious/spiritual resources.

312.4 assess the strengths and needs of those served, grounded in theology and using an understanding of the behavioral sciences.

312.5 manage ministry and administrative function in terms of accountability, productivity, self-direction, and clear, accurate professional communication.

312.6 demonstrate competent use of self in ministry and administrative function which includes: emotional availability, cultural humility, appropriate self-disclosure, positive use of power and authority, a non-anxious and non-judgmental presence, and clear and responsible boundaries.

Pastoral Reflection

312.7 establish collaboration and dialogue with peers, authorities and other professionals.

312.8 demonstrate self-supervision through realistic self-evaluation of pastoral functioning.

N2 (with tears) I could not sleep.

C3 You did not get good rest last night?

N3 No. (still teary) (*My heart goes out to her.*)

C4 I have learned about you in the last years that you need your rest to feel good. What was keeping you awake?

N4 Spirits.

C5 Spirits? (*I am curious to learn more about her experience.*)

N5 (She nods her head.)

C6 Would you like to tell me more about last night and the spirits?

N6 They are bad. (She makes a scared face.)

C7 Last night the bad spirits scared you?

N7 Yes. All week long.

C8 Every night this week you felt scared by the spirits. (*I try to understand what was disturbing her rest.*)

N8 (She nods.) Since Elsie came. (Elsie is her new roommate.)

C9 Elsie moved in on Monday. Since then you could not sleep at night and felt bad spirits? It is Thursday today. You must be very exhausted by now and upset about your new roommate.

N9 (new tears) I am so upset and scared.

C10 (I pull my chair a bit closer and gently put my hand on her hand which she has put on the table—silent moment.) Ms. N., you have been through a lot this week. (*I feel so sorry that she could not rest well. I would like to hear more about her experience in this week since Elsie moved in.*)

N10 (She nods and cries quietly.)

C11 What is it that makes you feel so bad?

N11 Elsie uses bad words. Loud. (*I am familiar with Elsie. She frequently talks to herself in a loud voice and often uses swear words.*)

C12 When Elsie uses bad words and speaks loudly you feel bad spirits are in your room?

N12 Yes. Because of her bad words.

C13 And then you feel scared. It sounds like you miss the peace and harmony you had with Nancy, your old roommate. (Nancy died a week ago on Friday.) (*I am sure Ms. N. is grieving the loss of her good roommate who also became a friend. I feel for her since Nancy has been one of several roommates who died since Ms. N. moved to the nursing home eight years ago.)*

N13 (She nods.) We had peace. Much peace. I miss that. (pause) I miss Nancy.

C14 (silent moment) I remember that you and Nancy got along so well (I reminisce a bit about their relationship. Ms. N. smiled) And now everything is different and you do not feel happy and peaceful anymore. And you miss your good friend Nancy. *(I miss Nancy too. She was such a serene person. Nancy and Ms. N. were a good match.)*

N14 (tears)

C15 *(I feel sad. There are so many deaths in the nursing home and constant adjustments needed.).* (We sit quietly.) *(I am thinking of the spirits that Ms. N. experienced. Often after a death of a resident the staff calls me to report spirits and asks for a traditional blessing. I wonder whether Ms. N. would find comfort in a blessing. Her sense of peace is clearly disturbed.)*

N15 (squeezing my hand)

C16 Ms. N. what would help you to feel better? You miss Nancy, have not slept in days, you are scared about bad spirits and are upset about Elsie.

N16 (She nods.) Thank you for coming. (silent moment) It helps.

C17 I am very glad to be here with you. (silent moment) I am concerned about your well-being.

N17 I don't feel peaceful anymore. (silent) What now?

C18 I am thinking of two things: One is for you to speak with J., the direc-tor of nursing about finding another roommate who is quieter. The other is to have a blessing of your room so peace may be restored. Would you like that?

N18 Yes. A blessing (pause) and talking to J.

C19 I will ask J. to visit with you so you may share your feelings and distress with her. I will come back this afternoon at 4 p.m. to bless your room. Is that a good time for you?

N19 Yes. (She smiles). Please come back. (silent) I feel better.

C20 Ms. N., I will be back this afternoon. See you later. (standing up and leaving)

N20 (She gives me a little wave.)

(I approach the director of nursing after my visit with Ms. N. She was already aware of the situation and had discussed switching roommates with the care team. She said she would talk with Ms. N. and find another roommate.)

I returned in the afternoon. Ms. N. was in her bed, watching TV. She was alone in her room. She waved me in, switched off the TV. She smiled when she saw the ti leaves, ocean water and Koa bowl.

N21 Good.

C21 I am here to bless your room.

N22 (smile) Yes. Peace again.

C22 Yes. (I sit down next to her bed after asking permission. I show her the elements of the Hawaiian blessing. Ms. N. is familiar with them. They have been part of her life in Hawaii. She also remembered the annual facility blessings in the nursing home. I invite her to pray with me. We remember Nancy with gratitude and pray for peace in this room, restored harmony, restful nights, harmonious relationships and bad spirits to vanish. She puts some salt in the blessing bowl and says: "Peace." Then I sprinkle the salt water with the ti leaves in her room. After that I sit with her for a while, quietly. Ms. N. falls asleep, looking peaceful.

Verbatim Analysis

I Holistic assessment[21]

1. *The medical dimension. What significant medical problems has the person had in the past? What problems do they have now? What treatment is the person receiving?*

   Ms. N. is a 94-year-old Japanese American woman. Before coming to this skilled nursing facility Ms. N. had a history of transient ischemic attacks (TIA). She was admitted eight years ago to the skilled nursing facility because she had suffered a massive stroke (brain attack) leaving her with decreased reflexes, decreased sensation and muscle weakness of the face, balance problems, problems turning her head to one side, weakness in her tongue and a slight problem in speaking, some memory deficits, urinary incontinence, inability to walk, and her left side (arm and leg) is paralyzed. She can still feed herself and enjoys doing arts and crafts with the functioning right hand and participates in physical therapy. For the last four days she reported

---

[21] I follow the 7x7 Model for Spiritual Assessment developed by George Fitchett, Ruth-Presbyterian-St. Luke's Medical Center, Chicago, Ill. See also: George Fitchett. *Assessing Spiritual Needs: A Guide for Caregivers* (Minneapolis: Augsburg Fortress, 1993).

problems sleeping (N2).

2. *The psychological dimension. Are there any significant psychological problems? Are they being treated? If so, how?*

Ms. N., despite her limitations due to her history with strokes, keeps up a positive outlook and attitude. She participates in many activities, has a strong sense of gratitude and is extremely cooperative and kind. She hardly complains and tries to bring a smile to other residents' faces. The fact that she expressed her negative feelings in this visit was rather unusual. I assess that Ms. N. is grieving the loss of her beloved roommate Nancy. She is in the ebb and flow of the dynamics of *grief*. After the *shock* of hearing about Nancy's death last Friday Ms. N gradually became aware of what has happened and began to express her emotions. When Elsie, the new roommate, moved in, Ms. N. began to feel and to hurt. She did not suppress her feelings but reported her discomfort to the RN and found some *emotional release* in meeting and sharing with the chaplain. Ms. N. expressed her feelings by talking about "spirits" (N4, N6). She *reported symptoms of some physical (N2) and emotional (N9, N13) distress* such as sleeplessness, feeling upset and scared, missing a sense of peace and missing the deceased Nancy. Psychiatrist John Bowlby[22] outlined the ebb and flow of grief processes such as shock and numbness, yearning and searching, disorganization and despair, and reorganization. I understand Ms. N is in a time of *disorganization and despair*. She lost her sense of feeling safe and secure with Nancy (N14).

3. *The Family Systems Dimension. Are there at present, or have there been in the past, patterns within the person's relationships with other family members which have contributed to or perpetuated present problems?*

Ms. N was born the last of three children to a Japanese immigrant couple. She is the only survivor. She married a Japanese American man and has one daughter and one granddaughter. Her husband died almost 20 years ago. The granddaughter is most active in caretaking of Ms. N. The family is extended with nephews and nieces who come to visit Ms. N. on a regular basis. The third generation does not speak Japanese anymore or only a little while Ms. N. is still bilingual. The family system is close-knit and caring, friendly, and positive. Being

---

[22] John Bowlby, "Process of Mourning," *International Journal of Psychoanalysis*, (42: 1961): 317–340.

relational, appreciative and in harmony are important values for Ms.
N.

4. *The Psycho-Social Dimension. What is the history of the person's life,
   including, place of birth and childhood home, family of origin, education,
   work history and other important activities and relationships? What is
   the person's present living situation and what are the person's financial
   resources?*

   Ms. N.'s mother came as a picture bride to Hawaii in 1908 when she
   was 18. She married a plantation worker and raised three children.
   Ms. N was the last born in 1913.[23]

5. *The Ethnic, Racial or Cultural Dimension. What is the person's racial,
   ethnic or cultural background? How does it contribute to the person's way
   of addressing any current concerns?*

   Ms. N. was born and raised on Oahu, Hawaii as nisei, second gen-

---

[23] *Background information:* Between 1885 and 1907, thousands of Japanese men came to Hawaii to
work on the sugarcane plantations in numbers so great that by 1897 the Japanese constituted the
largest single ethnic group in the islands. In 1888, there were 6,420 Japanese in Hawaii; in 1890,
12,360; in 1896, 24,407; in 1900, 61,111. By 1900, the Japanese comprised nearly 40 percent of
the population in Hawaii. They were not afraid of the hard plantation work—most were people
born in the rural districts of Japan and were familiar with grass-thatched huts, communal cooking
houses, communal baths, and physical isolation. The first major waves of Japanese "picture brides"
began in 1908 and before all immigration was stopped from Japan in 1924, these tens of thousands of women would reshape the Japanese community in Hawaii. In addition to being wives
and mothers who took care of the home, Japanese women immigrants also worked alongside their
husbands in the fields. This early period of stabilization of the Japanese family coincided with a
high birth rate. The birth of the second generation, the *nisei,* in effect established the identity of
the first generation, the issei who became responsible parents and were beginning to view the Hawaiian Islands as their new home. The establishment of families was soon followed by the growth
of Buddhist and Christian churches, a variety of language newspapers, and self-help organizations that served the needs of the immigrant community. After the 1920 plantation strike many
Japanese immigrants realized that the plantations were a system that offered them limited futures.
Thousands of laborers moved into the urban areas of Hawaii and began to enter the skilled trades,
small businesses and other non-agricultural fields that gave them economic freedom and opportunity. Neighborhood pockets were created as the Japanese community found ethnic solidarity
in their familiar associations. Clothing, food, customs, newspapers, stores and daily lifestyles of
the town of Honolulu began to clearly reflect the Asian character and influence of the Japanese
immigrants and their children.(Kayo Hatto in her film "The Picture Bride" (1994) tells the story
of picture brides in Hawaii.) Ms. N. was born a nisei, graduated from high school in Honolulu,
worked partially as a teacher for young children, married and raised one daughter. Her own and
her husband's family came from plantation-worker background but by hard work they became a
successful middle class family. Ms. N.'s husband worked in the banking business. Their cultural
identity development happened in two worlds, within their parents' traditional Japanese world
and the new world in Hawaii in the USA, with a desire to fit in, belong, not attract any attention
and be good citizens. This explains why Ms. N comes across as very polite and quiet.

eration Japanese in Hawaii. Ms. N. did not talk much about it but I assume that she, like many other nisei who lived in the period of World War II and internment went through a lot of hardship. Senator Daniel Inouye of Hawaii was 17 years old on December 7, 1941 (attack on Pearl Harbor), and later wrote: "The Japanese in Hawaii had wanted so desperately to be accepted, to be good Americans. Now, in a few cataclysmic minutes, it was all undone and there could only be deep trouble ahead. My people were only a generation removed from the land that had spawned the bombers and sent them to drop death on Hawaii."[24] Brian Sato, a local photographer, took photos of many nisei and spoke with them. He asked one woman what she would like to pass on to the younger generation, and she said "shimbo"—the strength to bear hardships and persevere. It's a stereotype, I know, but most of the nisei I met were quiet and reserved, with a lot of inner strength.[25] I can see this in Ms. N. as well, a quiet, reserved woman with lots of inner strength and perseverance. This is obvious in the way she deals with her physical struggles throughout the last years.

6. *The Social Issues Dimension. Are the present problems of the person created by or compounded by larger social problems or dysfunctions of which the person is largely a victim? If the person is in part suffering from larger social problems, can they become aware of them and join with others in efforts to address those problems?*

a) As described above in 5.), Ms. N. comes from a generation of Japanese Americans who experienced discrimination and hardship in WWII. To fit in and belong, to have peace and harmony are important values for Ms. N.

b) Living in a skilled nursing care facility, needing to share a room, needing to adjust to accepting help and being dependant are issues Ms. N. has to deal with, as well as facing multiple deaths and the loss of other residents. She is confronted with grief over and over. These are the facts of institutionalized care versus the family care model that Ms. N. has experienced in her Japanese upbringing.

---

[24] Senator Daniel Inouye, *Go for Broke* (WWII–100th/442nd), condensed from his autobiography, *Journey to Washington* (Englewood Cliffs, N.J.: Prentice Hall, 1967). *Go for Broke* is the story of Senator Daniel K. Inouye's experiences during World War II.

[25] Brian Sato's portraits of Hawaii's *nisei* were on display at the Japanese Cultural Center of Hawaii's Community Gallery in July 2007.

II Spiritual assessment

1. *Belief and Meaning. What does the person believe which gives meaning and purpose to their life? What major symbols reflect or express meaning for this person? What is the person's story? Are there any current problems which have a specific meaning or alter established meaning? Is the person presently or have they in the past been affiliated with a formal system of belief?*

   Ms. N said she and her family have always belonged to a temple in Honolulu of the Honpa Hongwanji Mission. Ms. N. said that she did not go to the temple that much but followed the main teachings. I learned that her generation lived faith by doing and practicing the teachings in ordinary things. When I offered to contact her temple and asked whether she would like to see members of her temple and/or the minister, Ms. N. declined. Ms. N. said she also grew up with many Christians in the area, and that she was never dogmatic about faith, but quite open. She stated that of main importance for her is that people act kindly, compassionately, respectfully, and with gratitude for life. Ms. N. occasionally joined some of the Christian Sunday worship services. Her granddaughter is the one in the family who nurtures the Buddhist roots. She brings in Buddhist teachings to her grandmother and Buddhist friends to visit the nursing home.[26]

2. *Vocation and Obligations. Do the person's beliefs and sense of meanings*

---

[26] *Background information:* The Honpa Hongwanji Mission of Hawaii is a district of the Nishi (West) Hongwanji, one of the major temples of Jodo Shinshu Buddhism, a school of Mahayana Pure Land Buddhism. Jodo Shinshu Buddhism was established in Hawaii as a result of the immigration of Japanese people to work the plantations on the islands. The first Hongwanji temple in Hawaii was dedicated in 1889. Since then, 36 temples and the Buddhist Study Center have been established statewide.

The Honpa Hongwanji Mission of Hawaii was initiated by Shinran Shonin (1173–1263), founder of Jodo Shin School on Pure Land Buddhism. Shinran Shonin was born during the Kamakura period in Japan. His teaching is based on the Pure Land tradition as a successor to Honen Shonin. Shinran Shonin concentrated his efforts on clarifying the necessity of being on the power of the Primal Vow as the inner dynamics of recitative nembutsu. The complete entrusting of self to the Primal Vow meant simultaneously abandoning all need to rely on self-power. This is the reason for Shinran's emphasis on Shinjin (Faith), "the true and real mind of Amida Buddha," which is the source of this entrusting. Through the working of Amida's wisdom and compassion, the followers are made to say the nembutsu, affirming the enduring power of Amida and acknowledging their limited human capacities. (Namu Amida Butsu—The original Sanskrit phrase was *Namo Amitabhaya Buddhaya*, which can mean either "I trust in the Buddha of Immeasurable Light and Eternal Life" or simply "Homage to the Buddha of Immeasurable Light and Eternal Life".) Thus, the central question for the Shin Buddhist becomes not "How can I attain satori (enlightenment)?" but "How can I be carried by the power of the Primal Vow?" Practices are: recitation of the nembutsu, bowing and gassho (putting hands together), chanting of Sutra, meditation and a life of gratitude, service and reverence. Motto: Embraced by the Vow ... In Harmony. (Introducto-

in life create a sense of duty, vocation, calling or moral obligation? Will any current problems cause conflict or compromise in their perception of their ability to fulfill these duties? Are any current problems viewed as a sacrifice or atonement or otherwise essential to this person's sense of duty?

"Embraced by the Vow … in Harmony" (see above) and living a life of gratitude and in reverence of life and service of others have always been central for Ms. N. She raised her family that way. Her role as mother and wife appear to have been central in her life. She also was an active volunteer in several women's service groups in her temple and community. Her current roommate can be loud, yells at times and uses bad words (N11). This disrupts Ms. N.'s need for harmony and peace (N13).

3.   *Experience and Emotion. What direct contacts with the sacred or divine or with the demonic has the person had? What emotions or moods are predominately associated with these contacts and with the person's beliefs, meaning in life and associated sense of vocation?*

Overall Ms. N. has experienced her faith as giving her peace and meaning in life. In this verbatim Ms. N. speaks of "spirits" (N4) as the reason for disruption of the harmony in her room and life. Experiencing "spirits" is very much part of the multicultural "local" culture in Hawaii, a blend of diverse traditions and beliefs related to the understanding of life, death and the afterlife.[27] Because Ms. N. grew up and lived in an environment that speaks about "spirits," it was not surprising that Ms. N. would describe her experience

---

ry Guide to Jodu Shinsu Buddhism as distributed by Honpa Hongwani Hawaii Betsuin, Honolulu, Hawaii, 1998 and notes from lecture by Rev. Mari Sengoku.).

[27] *Background information:* In Hawaiian tradition "the animating force ("uhane"), which is present in the body, distinguishes the quick from the dead. And so "uhane" can be called "spirit." It is a vital spark that, departed from the flesh, lives on through eternity and is rewarded for virtue or punished for transgressions in life. Thus "uhane" is spirit in the immortal sense. It might return to visit the living. "Uhane" could be more specifically an "aumakua", a god-spirit of a long-dead ancestor, an "unihipili, a deified spirit of a recently deceased person, an "akua", god or any demi-god. "Makani" is a chill breeze—and any Hawaiian knows that this breeze means a spirit is present. Therefore, "makani" is the spirit." (Mary Kawena Pukui, E.W. Haertig, C.A. Lee, *Nana I ke Kumu—Look to the Source* [Honolulu: Hui Hanai, 1972, Volume I], 195.) Ms. N. is familiar with the Hawaiian way of speaking about "spirit" and the many local stories coming from the plantation world. She also is familiar with her own tradition of addressing "spirits" such as in the "Obon season." "In Hawaii, the summer months are known for their annual Obon Dance Festivals held every weekend at various Buddhist Temples around the islands. It all begins in June with the an-nual lantern-floating ceremony and continues for nine weekends of Obon Dancing. The tradition is to light the way for the spirits of ancestors who are greeted with offerings of flowers, food and

of disharmony and lack of peace as caused by "spirits," especially considering the recent death of her roommate and the arrival of her seemingly restless and loud new roommate. Ms. N. described her feelings as "upset and scared" (N9).

4. *Courage and Growth. Must the meaning of new experiences, including any current problems, be fit into existing beliefs and symbols? Can the person let go of existing beliefs and symbols in order to allow new ones to emerge?*

    Ms. N's recent experience of disharmony and lack of peace cause her to feel upset and scared (N9) and disrupt her ability to sleep well (N2). Ms. N. is hurting because she misses her roommate (N13). To allow the journey of grief to interrupt her desire for peace and harmony may be an important step in the following weeks.

5. *Ritual and Practice. What are the rituals and practices associated with the person's beliefs and meaning in life? Will current problems, if any, cause a change in the rituals or practices they feel they require or in their ability to perform or participate in those which are important to them?*

    I suggested to Ms. N. a blessing of her room (C18) knowing that Ms. N. has experienced numerous blessings in the nursing home and in her life in the Hawaiian community. In Hawaii and in the nursing home this is a common ritual of cleansing and for comfort.[28]

6. *Community. Is the person part of one or more, formal or informal, com-*

---

incense in temple rituals and on family altars. The concept of dancing for the dead is based on a story about a disciple of the Buddha named Mokuren. The monk's vision of his dead mother in the realm of hungry ghosts, starving because of her greed while alive, led him to ask Shakyamuni Buddha how he could relieve her suffering. He was told to offer food to monks returning from a retreat. His mother's spirit was freed by his good deed, which led Mokuren to dance with joy. Although based on a Japanese religious belief, Bon Dances have become a favorite event celebrated in the islands by all different ethnic cultures and religious backgrounds." (See: http:// islandlife808.com/my-family/its-obon-season-in-hawaii/)

[28] *Background information:* Blessing is a very public event in Hawaii. Blessings are seen as being a serious event, a religious rite, and should not be taken lightly. It involves remembering traditions and utilizing common elements of water, salt (sea salt) and ti leaves (a green leafy plant used for healing and to plant near houses for good fortune). It is based in a spirituality in which the sea and land and the place of people are honored. The salt is added to the fresh water in a wooden bowl (Koa wood). The ti leaves are held at the stems and are used to stir the salt and the water and to sprinkle the water over the area or persons to be blessed by ways of snapping one's wrist and letting the salt water 'fly'. The use of salt, water and the ti leaves is to "purify an area or persons from spiritual contamination and remove kapus (taboos) and harmful influences...." The term used for the ritual is *pi kai*—*pi* is to sprinkle, *kai* means sea or sea water. (Pukui, *Nana I Ke Kumo*, 179.) The use of ti leaves was "thought to protect against harm and invoke protection of

munities of shared belief, meaning in life, ritual or practice? What is the style of the person's participation in these communities?

Ms. N.'s main community is her family who visits regularly and the "new family" in the nursing home. Ms. N. has become a leader in certain arts and crafts and received much recognition already for her talent and creativity. Some of her items were sold at the facility-wide craft fair. Her pleasantness and perseverance inspire other residents in the facility. In this sense Ms. N. has very much become a community-builder by her gentleness, positive attitude, and creativity in spite of her physical limitations. Ms. N. does not actively participate in her Buddhist temple, although her granddaughter has asked some of the temple members to come and visit Ms. N. As far as I know, Ms. N does not follow regular rituals consistent with her faith tradition, but practices the teachings of compassion and gratitude. She has regular visits from the facility chaplains.

7. *Authority and Guidance. Where does the person find authority for their beliefs, their meaning in life, their vocation, their rituals and practices? When faced with doubt, confusion, tragedy or conflict, where do they look for guidance? To what extent does the person look outside themselves or inside themselves for guidance?*

Ms. N. respects and trusts the chaplains and likes spending time with us. In a time of crisis as seen in this verbatim, Ms. N. is open to the chaplain/minister to help with restoring harmony. To live a "life of gratitude" as outlined in the teachings of her faith group has been her principle and source of meaning acknowledging the deliverance and benevolent guidance of Amida Buddha. Living in harmony with all beings is the way of Jodo Shin Buddhism.

III How did the chaplain feel about the patient/resident and/or situation?[29]

I felt warmth and caring for Ms. N. when entering the dining room. In these last eight years I have thoroughly enjoyed being in her kind presence. I was a bit concerned because of the charge nurse's referral since it was unusual for Ms. N "to be upset." She preferred to avoid any attention and focus on her. When I realized that Ms. N. was

---

the gods." (Ibid., 190.) Sprinkling salt water was a common practice not only in Hawaii but in many cultures, with salt having images of preserving, purifying, and flavoring, and water being seen as symbolic of purification and life-giving. Many Christian ministers have adapted this ritual. They use three ti leaves and sprinkle "In the name of the Father, the Son and the Holy Spirit."

[29] The verbatim analysis part III–VII follows a model used by Pacific Health Ministry, Hawaii, in CPE training.

grieving and feeling without peace, I felt protective of her. I wanted to make her feel better (C16). While Ms. N. was grateful for my visit and even said "it helps" (N16), I wanted to do more and suggested two more approaches: talk with the DON (Director of Nursing) and provide a blessing C18). I recognize my desire to take good care of Ms. N. and restore harmony again. I am grateful that in the context of Hawaii there is a blessing ritual in place for times like this. At the same time I know that the journey of grief can be like an emotional roller coaster. I will continue to support/accompany Ms. N. on this journey. And I will remember that I cannot take away the pain from Ms. N. despite my attempts and best efforts.

IV Are there unspoken or hidden dynamics that affect this interview? If so, what are they and how did they operate?

I have always admired Ms. N. for her serene and gentle presence in the nursing home. Considering her severe physical limitations after the major stroke, I have been so touched by her gracefulness amid suffering. I have been moved by her ability to accept her suffering and make the best of her new life in the nursing home. "Could I ever be like her?" I asked myself. I doubt it because I am much too attached at this time to my life. But I surely would like to be like Ms. N. Experiencing Ms. N. feeling "upset and scared" was new and surprising for me in our relationship. At the same time I could understand the dynamic of grief in her situation. So, I followed two dynamics: my need to make it all better (C18) and at the same time my knowing the need to create space and words to address the death of Nancy (C13, C14). To be effective I need to accept my inability to take away the pain of loss.

V How did the chaplain function and/or utilize the Spiritual Assessment in giving care?

I provided sensitive and respectful spiritual care utilizing the Spiritual Assessment (see above) and hearing Ms. N.'s need for harmony and peace. I offered a safe space for Ms. N. to share. I used reflective listening skills, acknowledged and explored her feelings of being upset, scared, and sleepless. I built on our pastoral relationship and history, offering a ministry of presence. I provided spiritual resources appropriate for the context and situation and blessed her room. I made sure that the Director of Nursing and the interdisciplinary care team were involved.

It was important for me, while providing spiritual care, to touch

Ms. N.'s grieving heart. In N8 Ms. N. gave me the connection that with the arrival of her new roommate the loss of her old roommate became obvious. It became difficult for Ms. N. to escape her feelings. I tried to understand the meaning of "spirits" (N4) and of the arrival of the roommate (N8) and to walk with Ms. N. through the related feelings (scared, N6, N9; upset, N8; tears, N10). It is a slow process until in C13 I finally named the real issue, that is, missing the peace and harmony with Nancy (N13 "I miss Nancy."). This is followed by reminiscing about Nancy and their relationship (C14) and more tears (N14). I was intentional in assisting Ms. N. in addressing her emotional ties to Nancy despite the discomfort and sorrow it causes. I wanted Ms. N. to feel free to express her grief (C14). "What a griever needs most is acceptance and non-judgmental listening, which will facilitate the expression of emotions and the necessary review of the relationship with a lost loved one. The griever will then require assistance in integrating the past with the new present that exists."[30]

While Ms. N. described her experience of disorganization in this early stage of grief (N2, N6, N9, C14), I offered my presence, a sense of security and support to help her to reorient to a world that has gone out of focus and control with the death of Nancy. The appropriate physical contact in C10, N15 also provided support as well as several moments of just "being" together quietly but connected (N10, C15, C17). Ms. N. responded well to "just being," "not doing" (C16, C17). Yet, I wanted "to do" more. I knew that Ms. N. did not have any closing ritual at the time of her friend's death. Nancy died in the hospital. When the residents die in the nursing home the chaplains offer bedside services for the staff and other residents. A traditional blessing of the room seemed called for as a ritual of closure and blessing of the new beginning. Ms. N. responded well to it (C22) and participated with the salt. As mentioned above, my own need of wanting "to do" more played into offering a ritual; but more important was my knowledge about the importance of rituals in times of grief and in Hawaii. Rituals can give structure and support in a time of loss and transition. I hoped that for Ms. N. the blessing would be helpful in managing her sense of disorganization and loss of control.

---

[30] Therese A. Rando, *Grief, Dying and Death* (Champaign, IL: Research Press, 1984),p. 79.

VI What are the plans for continued care and follow up?

I spoke with the Director of Nursing about Ms. N.'s roommate and will continue to work with the interdisciplinary care team. I will continue to visit Ms. N. and accompany her on her journey of grief. I will assist her in accessing and utilizing internal coping strategies to reorganize and incorporate the loss and in using her existing spiritual resources (e.g. Buddhist teachings) to reshape a sense of safety and security, by this means incorporating the changes that have occurred in her life.

VII What did the chaplain learn about the chaplain's faith, religious understandings, self-awareness, and caregiving?

I felt humbled that Ms. N. invited me to share her spiritual struggles, lack of peace and harmony, and her grief with me. As a Christian pastor from Germany serving as chaplain in an interfaith context in Hawaii, I am consistently challenged to learn as much as possible and be knowledgeable about the meaning making, history, stories, many faith traditions and practices here. This is shown in this verbatim about "spirits," nisei, Honpa Hongwanji Mission and traditional blessings. This is not clear-cut book learning, but the art of finding a "meeting place/space of exchange" in this process is important to me. The "between" becomes an essential dimension for spiritual care. As with Ms. N., offering a ministry of presence worked well, a ministry that is based on empathetic and compassionate care. I need to be authentic, genuine, warm, and real. I have experienced many Buddhist residents and patients as welcoming—just like Ms. N. Kindness and gentleness, open ears and mind, a listening heart, respect without judgment, and creating a space to share have been appreciated by the patients, families, and friends.

As a Christian spiritual caregiver I ask myself how to evaluate theologically the interfaith situation and interaction with the patients. Jesus is my model for healing relationships, love, dialogue, respect, and forgiveness. Through Christ I know that God reaches out in love to *all*. I am called to walk the path of holiness that Jesus showed me (he reached out to the Samaritans, "lepers", bleeding women, sinners, the poor ...). God shows the face of mercy and love. I must be subject to all human beings, a servant, God's willing instrument. Jesus healed the ones in need, the marginalized. He loved them, ate with them, touched them, comforted them, blessed them, served them, encouraged them, taught them, and liberated them by his own suffering, death, and resurrection. Finally, Jesus breathed on them to infuse them with the power of the Holy Spirit. Jesus, full of compassion, journeyed with people.

Dialogue is about listening and learning rather than about arguing and convincing, and not about converting. It does not start with doctrines. It is not about labeling, but seeing through the eyes of compassion. It is about storytelling and listening. The Sufi poet Rumi said once: "Out beyond ideas of wrongdoing and right doing, there is a field. I'll meet you there."[31] Ms. N. and I met on this "field," a place to hear about gloom and sadness, a place to re-invite peace and harmony through the gift of the "I and Thou" relationship and meeting dynamic[32] and the power and mystery of ritual.

---

[31] Marshall B. Rosenberg, *Nonviolent Communication: A Language of Life* (Encinitas, CA: Puddle Dancer Press, 2003), p. 15.

[32] See Martin Buber's classic book, *I and Thou* (New York: Scribner, 1958).

Epilogue
Becoming wise interfaith spiritual caregivers

The following paragraphs present a picture of excellence and growth in *professional wisdom*. They highlight concisely a number of practical guidelines that are considered and illustrated in this book. We will thus conclude the discussion of interfaith spiritual care in health care institutions with a profile of competence that describes our common and ongoing vocational commitment.

Wisdom in interfaith care involves not only what we know but also what we are and what we do. In other words, professional wisdom for quality interfaith care may be viewed as the integration of three interconnected domains—*knowing, being* and *doing,* as represented below.[1] And this is the case concerning both the "clinical" dimensions (i.e. attitudes, knowledge and skills that define expertise) as well as "ministerial" dimensions (i.e. vocational identity, adequate philosophy of care and consistent practice) connoted in the term, *professional.* We thus propose that a portrait can be drawn by focusing on a number of core *competencies* within each of those domains. The resulting profile of wise spiritual care consists of three sets of core competencies which we have identified as such in the course of our own spiritual care practice, research work, and extensive collegial consultation and collaboration.

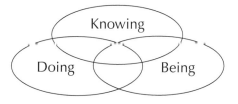

Competencies are those dispositions and capacities necessary to care

---

[1] For the following understanding of "professional wisdom" in terms of knowing, being, and doing, we are partially indebted to John Patton's thought as presented in *Pastoral Care: An Essential Guide* (Nashville: Abingdon Press, 2006), chapters 1,2,3.

well in interfaith situations. Therefore, core competencies thus viewed correlate with professional *standards* normally articulated by organizations such as the Association for Clinical Pastoral Education and the Canadian Association for Spiritual Care among others, or by governmental or ecclesiastic institutions. The standards embody key values and vocational commitments; they also identify certain legally binding professional and ethical requirements for effective care giving. In sum, competencies are those personal and professional qualities or assets with which care givers meet the standards of practice in a wide variety of care giving settings.

Interestingly, a number of practitioners and researchers in the wider field of care and counseling have similarly presented three sets of core competencies. This is the case, for example, with the significant contribution of Derald Wing Sue and David Sue concerning multicultural competence in counseling practice. These authors discuss fourteen competencies under the categories of *awareness* (e.g., being aware of, and sensitive to one's own cultural heritage and to valuing and respecting differences); *knowledge* (e.g., becoming knowledgeable and informed on a number of culturally diverse groups, especially groups with which therapists work); and *skills* (e.g., being able to generate a wide variety of verbal and nonverbal helping responses).[2] Other authors have integrated the contribution of Sue and Sue and others in their own three-fold characterization in terms of (a) caregivers' awareness of their own values and biases, (b) understanding of the clients' worldview, and (c) developing culturally appropriate intervention strategies and techniques.[3] For their part, some health care organizations also present a tripartite view of core competencies as "the essential knowledge, skills and attitudes necessary for the practice of …care"[4]

Those considerations are very useful and, indeed, transferable in principle when focusing on interfaith care giving. At the same time, we believe that the larger categories of *being, knowing,* and *doing,* can help us to present a more complete view of professional wisdom. That is especially the case regarding the "being" dimension, because in it we include competencies definable in terms of virtues (viewed as values embodied in the caregiver's character) and faith development, which are not explicitly considered in current discussions and writings in the field. A helpful conceptualization of "character strengths"—the psycho-

---

[2] Derald Wing Sue and David Sue. *Counseling the Culturally Diverse: Theory and Practice,* 5th ed.. (Hoboken, N.J.: John Wiley & Sons, 2008), 42-52.
[3] Gerald Corey, Marianne Schneider Corey, and Patrick Callanan. *Issues and Ethics in the Helping Professions.* (Belmont, CA.: Brooks/Cole/Thomson Learning, 2007), 141-148.
[4] Public Health Agency of Canada. Core Competencies for Public Health Service in Canada (Otawa: Ministry of Health, 2008), 1.

logical ingredients and processes that define the "virtues"—coming from the Positive Psychology movement, however, is available for spiritual caregivers to consider.[5]

Competencies of *knowing (understanding)*

In order to grow in pastoral wisdom, spiritual caregivers participate in what we might call "circles of learning" that include four dimensions: actual experience of being cared for and caring for others (learning by "feeling"); observation and reflection on care provided by others (learning by actively "seeing" and "hearing"); systematic analysis of those practices of care (learning by "thinking"); and active experimentation with new ways of caring well for others (learning by "doing"). The more intentionally and consistently we participate in the four dimensions of the "circle," the more likely that our knowing of interfaith care will increase. Therefore supervision, seminars and consultation groups are fertile settings for developing knowledge and understanding related to spiritual care in interfaith situations.[6] A sample of indicators of professional wisdom directly connected with this domain (*knowing*), include the following:

- A philosophy of spiritual care, including a view of human wholeness, truth, the good life, and excellence in professional work (as seen especially in an ethic of care), grounded in one's faith tradition.

- Optimal theoretical integration of spirituality, human science and theological perspectives.

- Understanding of the complexities, dynamics and richness of interfaith situations, with appreciation for human and spiritual commonalities and due consideration to gender, culture, religious, family and social and political contexts.

- Theological assessment that includes: revisiting the validity of certain absolute, normative doctrinal claims; selective reappropriation of theological and religious convictions; rediscovery of

---

[5] See Christopher Peterson and Martin E. P. Seligman. *Character Strengths and Virtues: A Handbook and Classification.* American Psychological Association. (New York: Oxford Press, 2004), 12-31.

[6] We (the editors) co-led a year-long seminar group jointly sponsored by the Associated Mennonite Biblical Seminary and the Pastoral Care Department of Lutheran Hospital of Indiana in 2006–2007. We have also presented numerous workshops on interfaith spiritual care in different settings in Canada, the USA, and Europe. In those events, activities aimed at increasing the theoretical and practical-clinical knowledge of interfaith spiritual care included actual caregiving practice, preparation and analysis of spiritual care situations, group and individual supervision of caregiving practice, discussion of readings and special topics of concern, and engagement in conversation and study with other health care professionals.

the simplicity and beauty of core spiritual clues for interfaith care, etc.

- Linguistic-conceptual and "multilingual" competency (knowing a variety of psychological, theological and spiritual languages) born out of theological and human science perspectives and resources.

- Clinical ways of knowing, such as interpretive frameworks (psychodynamic, systemic, etc.), that enhance understanding, communication, and ministerial practice of spiritual care.

Such comprehensive ways of *knowing* in turn must always be closely related to the *being* and *doing* dimensions of professional wisdom, as briefly considered in the following two sections.

Competencies of *being (presence)*

Professional wisdom is also a matter of "being" as well as "being with" that defines *presence*. Caregiving in interfaith situations involves special sensitivity and self-awareness regarding what one feels and experiences in the relationship. It also involves the sense that one represents not only a religious tradition and community but also, somehow, healing Grace. Indeed we deem such embodiment essential to remind care receivers that a caring Presence is available. Therefore, the sense of personal and professional (ministerial) identity is an essential component of being and presence. It is in fact indispensable to engage the care receiver in a relationship characterized first of all by respectful attending and listening. Such relationship allows the spiritual caregiver to be a witness, not primarily to "tell" things, let alone to tell care receivers how to cope with or fix their situation, but rather to "admire," to behold with love and hope the mystery that is the stranger. Among the traits related to the *being* dimension of professional wisdom, we find the following essential:

- Self-awareness, and other indicators of emotional intelligence, including: acknowledgment of strengths and limitations; movement beyond preoccupation with one's "ministerial-therapeutic" self (while maintaining clarity regarding identity as spiritual caregiver); and recognition of ways in which that ministerial self influences the interfaith encounter.

- Moral character—in the sense of desirable, good "heart" qualities for caring well, or *orthopathy* (complementing *orthodoxy*, true beliefs; and *orthopraxis*, right actions)—that integrates a plurality of attitudes and virtues such as capacity for wonder and respect in the face of the stranger; sensitivity and receptivity; courage to risk and to be surprised; freedom to be vulnerable and open to learning and growth; disposition to recognize, accept, and honor those deemed to be different; hospitality grounded in compassion, humility, and generosity; passion to care and creative energy to transform the inherent violence of separation, prejudice, and alienation into a way of being with (empathy) and for (sympathy) the other as neighbor and partner in care and healing.

- Spirituality defined in part in terms of a "conjunctive faith" which informs ministry style. We have adopted the concept of *conjunctive faith* as presented by James W. Fowler.[7] which denotes a desirable level of faith development, briefly characterized here in terms of: ability to embrace ambiguity and paradox; a sense of truth that is multiform and complex; post-critical receptivity ("second naiveté") and readiness to participate in the reality expressed in symbols, myths and rituals of one's own tradition; genuine and disciplined openness to the truths of communities and traditions other than one's own (not to be equated with relativism); move-ment from the prevalence of certainty to the centrality of trust.

- Sense of personal and spiritual wellbeing, integrity and growth. While being aware of their own woundedness, wise spiritual caregivers normally experience holistic wellness of body, soul and spirit, and an existentially fruitful and fulfilling life journey.

- Experience of connection with a transcendent Source of love and grace. Christian spiritual caregivers often define such connection as partnership with the Spirit of God or Holy Spirit to whom they actually attribute the power to heal even in the face of suffering and death.

Competencies of *doing (companioning)*

Accompaniment and *guidance* are words that name well what we actually do in spiritual care. On the one hand, spiritual caregivers are responsible for attending to, and guiding the actual caregiving process as such. In that sense, guidance is a form of leading which includes, for example, setting appropriate boundaries of time, space, contact, and remaining fully aware of what is going on in the caregiving process. Guidance may of course include gently probing questions, encouragement and support,

---

[7] See especially, James H. Fowler, *Stages of Faith: The Psychology of Human Development and the Quest for Meaning* (San Francisco: Harper & Row, 1981), 184-198; and *Faith Development and Pastoral Care* (Philadelphia: Fortress Press, 1987), 71-74, 92-98.

instructing, confronting, and mediating. On the other hand, except in certain emergency or crisis situations, spiritual caregivers will not be directive and try to resolve the problems and struggles faced by care receivers. Especially in interfaith situations, wise caregivers will rather help patients and others to use the specific spiritual resources that have been part of their lives or that may be now available for them. In short, accompaniment and guidance will optimally be a practice of wisdom—to know how to relate and act in order to care well in interfaith situations. There is actually an interesting etymological connection between *wisdom* and *guidance*. In English, the words wisdom and wise derive from an Indo-European root, *weid-*, which means *to see* or *to know*. They are related to the Greek *eidos* (idea, form, seeing), to the Latin *videre* (to see), and to the modern German *wissen* (to know). And the word *guide* comes from an ancient Romanic word, *widare*, which means to know. The words *wise*, *wisdom*, *wit*, and *guide*, all share the same origin. Therefore, among other competencies and skills, effective caregivers will be able to:

- Relate to care-seekers, their relatives, and colleagues in ways that engage their spirituality and facilitate spiritual assessment, including the skill to articulate desired outcomes of spiritual care.

- Internally monitor ongoing caregiving practice so as to remain care receiver-centered, avoid cultural and spiritual invasion or intrusiveness, and be open to receiving manifold gifts from care receivers even as we care well for them.

- Actively listen and discern the appropriateness and timeliness of specific caregiving gestures, use of language and action.

- Fittingly provide specific opportune responses in a variety of caregiving modes (e.g. probing, supporting, encouraging, comforting, guiding, confronting, mediating, reconciling, evoking, advocating; praying, blessing, anointing, and others).

- Reflect pastorally-theologically on ministerial practice on an ongoing basis and continually develop a practical theology of interfaith care.

- Actively partner with the transcendence Source of love and grace/Spirit of God while anticipating and participating in caregiving ministry (e.g. by privately praying for oneself and for care seekers, engaging in contemplation and meditation, and other spiritual disciplines).

- Regularly connect with colleagues for support and accountability.

- Maintain patterned practices (i.e. discipline) of self-care with adequate attention to physical, emotional and relational needs and to spiritual nourishment.

Holistic professional formation

It has become more and more apparent that the education of interfaith spiritual caregivers in professional wisdom requires that theological education and ministerial formation be holistic and comprehensive. Such formation must include three equally important and interrelated aspects, namely, academic, personal-spiritual, and professional, as briefly noted below. Further, such education must include specific pedagogies of interpretation and contextualization, formation, and performance.

The *academic* formation of interfaith caregivers is obviously indispensable because, among other contents, it includes learning about one's own (religious or nonreligious) faith tradition and heritage and as much as possible about other traditions. Philosophies, theoretical frameworks and other resources stemming from the human sciences are of course also indispensable. Academic formation further includes learning about the social and cultural, and institutional contexts of caregiving work. Therefore, this dimension of education and ministerial formation must focus primarily, although by no means exclusively, on learning and developing the competencies of *knowing* for wise caregiving, as highlighted above.

The *personal-spiritual* formation focuses on the identity and integrity of interfaith spiritual caregivers primarily but not exclusively as representatives of a given tradition. Personal-spiritual formation primarily involves attention to oneself as a human and spiritual being and on nurturing one's moral character and one's vocation in particular. Hence, this dimension of education and ministerial formation is concerned primarily with fostering and nurturing the competencies of *being* for wise ministry practice. Indeed, those competencies will directly inform the content of specific curricular learning goals towards personal/spiritual formation.

The *vocational-professional* formation of wise spiritual caregivers centers on the development of those clinical and other habits, skills, methods and approaches necessary for caring effectively and faithfully wherever they serve. Therefore, the third aspect of theological education and ministerial formation of interfaith spiritual caregivers must focus primarily on the development and practice of competencies of performance—that is, the *doing* dimension of the profile—as main curricular goal.

Those three resulting sets of goals of theological education and ministerial formation must in turn be kept in mind and must be duly integrated and approached with appropriate, mutually complementary pedagogies. In fact, recent reflection on pedagogies for educating clergy can be helpfully applied to the formation of wise spiritual caregivers as succinctly and generally described below.[8]

Pedagogies of interpretation focus the attention of caregivers as interpreters on their interaction with their tradition and with other sources of knowledge, and their relationship with care seekers in particular. Especially, they seek to foster the abilities to adequately "read" and analyze human situations, and to think and reflect critically and creatively. They are aimed at expanding and deepening *understanding* through interpretive practice. Pedagogies of contextualization are closely related, as they seek to develop the spiritual caregivers' consciousness of context, the ability to participate constructively in the encounter of diverse contexts, and to engage in the transformation of contexts (e.g. improvement of hospital culture).

Pedagogies of formation are aimed at fostering personal integrity and professional identity. Specific strategies that contribute to the formation of ministering caregivers, especially those who represent certain religious traditions, may include: awakening students to the presence of God; practicing holiness, that is, nurturing those dispositions and habits that embody religious commitments integral to the identity of ministering persons; and practicing religious leadership whose very *presence* communicates Grace and Wisdom.

Pedagogies of performance focus on the interaction of academic and religious expectations for effective leadership in ministerial practice. They seek to prepare caregivers to be adequately proficient in meeting a wide variety of expectations for excellence in interfaith care. In sum, they are learning strategies aimed at equipping caregivers for the ministry art of *companioning*.

Growth in professional wisdom in light of the increasing plurality of faith traditions and expressions (both religious and nonreligious) among care seekers and others has become an overarching goal in the formation, performance evaluation, and continuing education of spiritual caregivers. Therefore, we hope that this book and our summary discussion of core competencies will contribute to the efforts to enhance spiritual care in hospitals and other health care centers. For our part, we remain committed to further dialogue and collaboration with other interested practitioners, researchers, theological and clinical educators, and administrators in the days ahead.

---

[8] Charles R. Foster, Lisa E. Dahill, Lawrence A. Golemon, and Barbara Wang Tolentino. *Educating Clergy: Teaching Practices and Pastoral Imagination* (San Francisco: Jossey-Bass, 2006), 67-186

Caring Well

Interfaith spiritual care as professional responsibility

Leah Dawn Bueckert and Daniel S. Schipani

Spiritual caregivers in health care settings are committed to caring well for people of all faith traditions by integrating our theological understanding of ministry with the codes of conduct espoused by the profession and the institutions in which we serve. Highlighted below are some of the ethical standards related to responsibility in multi-faith contexts as articulated by the United States' Association of Clinical Pastoral Education (ACPE), the Canadian Association for Spiritual Care (CASC)/Association Canadienne des Soins Spirituels (ACSS), and the Association of Professional Chaplains (APC). These are professional associations in North America that provide education and certification in spiritual care. The codes of ethics are intended to inform members' relationships to those served, colleagues and other members, the professional association, and their faith group, among others.

Increasingly, the patients, communities, and colleagues that we relate to are people from a multiplicity of cultures and religious traditions. Chaplains recognize that the professional codes of conduct by which we abide call us to honor the human dignity and faith of all those we meet. Christian chaplains also acknowledge that this very care rises out of our own faith and ministry commitments.[1]

---

[1] For example, the mission statement of the National Association of Catholic Chaplains (NACC) affirms its support of "chaplains, clinical pastoral educators, and all members who continue the healing ministry of Jesus in the name of the Church." The acronym DISCIPLE synthesizes the eight core values of the NACC: *discipleship* (reflecting on and following the mission of Jesus); *integrity* (living out the Gospel in all we do); *stewardship* (developing and utilizing wisely the gifts and resources entrusted to us); *compassion* (responding to the call of Jesus by sharing the suffering, joy, and hope of others); *inclusivity* (welcoming, honoring, and fostering diversity that deepens unity); *professionalism* (competent and effective spiritual care ministry); *leadership* (collaborating to develop and nurture the necessary gifts for the direction of caregiving ministry); and *empowerment* (encouraging others to use their gifts within and beyond professional spiritual care). From the Association's website: http://www.nacc.org

The three organizations mentioned above present converging themes related to interfaith care that can be highlighted here. First, each upholds the importance of showing respect for the religious convictions of those served and places emphasis on not imposing one's own theology or cultural values. The APC code states, "members shall affirm the religious and spiritual freedom of all persons." What is promoted here is the acknowledgment that, though different than our own, the spiritual convictions of others hold truth and guidance for living well. This is not the same as saying that all convictions have equal value or that anything goes. There may sometimes be a place for chaplains to humbly engage in "critical caring," that is, challenging beliefs and practices that are detrimental to healing and wholeness, for example the belief that forgiveness is not available. All of us have the propensity to be misguided and sometimes this includes our interpretation or application of certain religious tenets. This is why we approach each person we meet believing that we have something to learn from them.

Second, all three codes include a reference to the importance of pursuing ongoing professional and personal education and growth. Even as we practice guidance with care receivers and co-workers, we acknowledge that we are also constantly growing and learning. This is particularly significant for a commitment to interfaith caregiving. The more we become aware of the particularities and values of people from a variety of religious traditions, the more sensitively we can provide pastoral care. But, more important than head-knowledge about other religions, is our demeanor and willingness to open ourselves to the possibility of divine revelation in our encounter with the other.

Third, each of the codes encourages members to work out concerns face to face with the people involved, in a spirit of collegiality and mutual respect. This is significant for interfaith care because, the more we are willing and able to express ourselves openly and hear where the other person is coming from, the less likely we are to keep them at a distance. In fact, the Ethics Commission of the Association for Clinical Pastoral Education (ACPE) "has revised both the Code and its administrative processes using the lens of restorative rather than retributive justice."[2] The restorative justice approach to addressing ethical conflicts involves hearing from all parties and includes questions about the broader contexts of the individuals involved. It is important for interfaith spiritual caregivers to keep in mind the community and family contexts of care

---

[2] Anne Underwood, Esq., "Restorative Justice as a Model for the ACPE Ethics Process," in ACPE's website, http://www.acpe.edu.

receivers. The commitment to address concerns face-to-face rises out of the conviction that relationships thrive when concerns for both harmony and justice are held in balance. As interfaith spiritual caregivers, we strive to make meaningful connections with those we serve and work alongside while also offering ourselves as advocates especially with those who are vulnerable or marginalized.

Caring well rises out of what is becoming known as the "ethic of care [which is] a reminder that mutual interdependence in relationships is the foundation and goal of moral decision making and responsibility. Concerns for both peace and justice are integral to an ethic of care, especially when these concerns are grounded biblically and theologically."[3] Christian chaplains are called, both professionally and pastorally, to learn and grow in the ways of interfaith spiritual care.

Following are excerpts from the three codes as they relate to interfaith care with emphasis added.

Code of professional ethics for ACPE members[4]

Standard 100

Maintenance of high standards of ethical conduct is a responsibility shared by all ACPE members and students. ACPE members agree to adhere to a standard of conduct consistent with the code of ethics established in ACPE standards. Members are required to sign the *Accountability For Ethical Conduct Policy Report Form* and to promptly provide notice to the ACPE Executive Director of any complaint of unethical or felonious conduct made against them in a civil, criminal, ecclesiastical, employment, or another professional organization's forum. Any ACPE member may invoke an ethics, accreditation or certification review process when a member's conduct, inside or outside their professional work involves an alleged abuse of power or authority, involves an alleged felony, or is the subject of civil action or discipline in another forum when any of these impinge upon the ability of a member to function effectively and credibly as a CPE supervisor, chaplain or spiritual care provider.

Standard 101 In relationship to those served, ACPE members
101.1 affirm and respect the human dignity and individual worth of each person.
101.2 do not discriminate against anyone because of race, gender, age,

---

[3] See "The Ethic of Care in Spiritual Caregiving," in Leah Dawn Bueckert and Daniel S. Schipani, editors, *Spiritual Caregiving in the Hospital: Windows to Chaplaincy Ministry* (Kitchener: Pandora Press, 2006), 233-44.

[4] ACPE website: http://www.acpe.edu

faith group, national origin, sexual orientation, or disability.
101.3 respect the integrity and welfare of those served or supervised, refraining from disparagement and avoiding emotional exploitation, sexual exploitation, or any other kind of exploitation.
101.4 approach the religious convictions of a person, group and/or CPE student with respect and sensitivity; avoid the imposition of their theology or cultural values on those served or supervised.
101.5 respect confidentiality to the extent permitted by law, regulations or other applicable rules.
101.6 follow nationally established guidelines in the design of research involving human subjects and gain approval from a recognized institutional review board before conducting such research.

Standard 102 In relation to other groups, ACPE members
102.1 maintain good standing in their faith group.
102.2 abide by the professional practice and/or teaching standards of the state, the community and the institution in which they are employed. If, for any reason they are not free to practice or teach according to conscience, they shall notify the employer and ACPE through the regional director.
102.3 maintain professional relationships with other persons in the ACPE center, institution in which employed and/or the community.
102.4 do not directly or by implication claim professional qualifications that exceed actual qualifications or misrepresent their affiliation with any institution, organization or individual; are responsible for correcting the misrepresentation or misunderstanding of their professional qualifications or affiliations.

Standard 103 In relation to ACPE, members
103.1 continue professional education and growth, including participation
in the meetings and affairs of ACPE.
103.2 avoid using knowledge, position or professional association to secure unfair personal advantage; do not knowingly permit their services to be used by others for purposes inconsistent with the ethical standards of ACPE; or use affiliation with ACPE for purposes that are not consistent with ACPE standards.
103.3 speak on behalf of ACPE or represent the official position of ACPE only as authorized by the ACPE governing body.
103.4 do not make intentionally false, misleading or incomplete state-

ments about their work or ethical behavior when questioned by colleagues.

Standard 104 In collegial relationships, ACPE members
104.1 respect the integrity and welfare of colleagues; maintain professional relationships on a professional basis, refraining from disparagement and avoiding emotional, sexual or any other kind of exploitation.
104.2 take collegial and responsible acion when concerns about incompetence, impairment or misconduct arise.

Standard 105 In conducting business matters, ACPE members
105.1 carry out administrative responsibilities in a timely and professional manner.
105.2 implement sound fiscal practices, maintain accurate financial records and protect the integrity of funds entrusted to their care.
105.3 distinguish private opinions from those of ACPE, their faith group or profession in all publicity, public announcements or publications.
105.4 accurately describe the ACPE center, its pastoral services and educational programs. All statements in advertising, catalogs, publications, recruiting, and academic calendars shall be accurate at the time of publication. Publications advertising a center's programs shall include the type(s) and level(s) of education offered, and the ACPE address, telephone number and website address.
105.5 accurately describe program expectations, including time requirements, in the admissions process for CPE programs.

Standard 200 Complaints
ACPE encourages persons to work out concerns or grievances informally, face-to-face, and in a spirit of collegiality and mutual respect. If differences are not resolved, a complaint involving an alleged violation of the ACPE ethical or professional standards may be registered in accordance with the procedures set forth in the manual *Processing Complaints of Ethics Code Violations.*

The Professional Ethics Commission has final authority to determine whether violations of ACPE standards have occurred and to determine final disposition of complaints. Policies and procedures for registering a complaint, conducting mediation and hearings, and disposing of complaints are found in *Processing Complaints of Ethics Code Violations.*

CASC/ACSS[5] Code of Ethics for Chaplains, Pastoral Counselors, Pastors, Pastoral Educators and Students hereinafter referred to as: Spiritual Care Professionals

The Code of Ethics for Spiritual Care Professionals: gives expression to the basic values and standards of the profession; guides decision making and professional behavior; provides a mechanism for professional accountability; and informs the public as to what they should expect from Spiritual Care Professionals.

Preamble

CAPPE/ACPEP gathers together Spiritual Care Professionals who are grounded in communities of faith and informed by professional education and training.

They are called to nurture their personal health of mind, body and spirit and be responsible for their personal and professional conduct as they grow in their respect for all living beings and the natural environment. When Spiritual Care Professionals behave in a manner congruent with the values of this code of ethics, they bring greater justice, compassion and healing to our world.

Spiritual Care Professionals:

affirm the dignity and value of each individual;
respect the right of each faith group to hold to its values and traditions;
advocate for professional accountability that protects the public and advances the profession; and *respect the cultural, ethnic, gender, racial, sexual-orientation, and religious diversity of other professionals and those served and strive to eliminate discrimination.*

1.0 Ethical Principles in Relationships with "Clients"

Spiritual Care Professionals understand "clients" to be any counselees, congregants, prisoners, patients and their family members, students or staff to whom they provide spiritual care.

In relationships with "clients," Spiritual Care Professionals uphold the following standards of professional ethics. Spiritual Care Professionals:

---

[5] (Association canadienne pour la pratique et l'éducation pastorales) website: http://www.cappe. org. The name of this organization is in the process of being changed to Canadian Association for Spiritual Care/Association Canadienne des soins Spirituels.

1.1 Speak and act in ways that honor the dignity and value of every individual.

1.2 Provide care that is intended to promote the best interest of the client and to foster strength, integrity and healing.

1.3 Demonstrate respect for the cultural and religious values of those they serve and refrain from imposing their our own values and beliefs on those served.

1.4 Are mindful of the imbalance of power in the professional/client relationship and refrain from exploitation of that imbalance.

1.5 Maintain relationships with current clients on a professional basis only.

1.6 There will be no sexual or other intimate relationships with former clients.

1.7 Avoid or correct any conflicts of interest or appearance of conflicting interest(s).

1.8 Refrain from any form of sexual misconduct, sexual harassment or sexual assault in relationships with clients.

1.9 Refrain from any form of harassment, coercion, intimidation or otherwise abusive words or actions in relationships with clients.

1.10 Safeguard the confidentiality of clients when using materials for educational purposes or written publication.

1.11 Respect the confidentiality of information entrusted to them by clients when communicating with family members or significant others except when disclosure is required for necessary treatment, granted by client permission, for the safety of any person or when required by law.

1.12 Understand the limits of their individual expertise and make referrals to other professionals when appropriate.

1.13 Provide clear expectations regarding responsibilities, appointment schedules, fees and payments.

2.0 Ethical Principles in Relationships Between Supervisors/Educators and Staff/ Students

Spiritual Care Professionals respect the integrity of their employees or students using the power they have as managers/directors or supervisors/educators in responsible ways. Spiritual Care Professionals:

2.1 Maintain a healthy educational or work environment, free of coercion or intimidation.

2.2 Maintain clear ethical boundaries in the areas of self-disclosure, intimacy and sexuality.

2.3 Provide clear expectations regarding responsibilities, work schedules, fees and payments.

2.4 Provide adequate, timely and constructive feedback to students and complete regular performance appraisals for their staff.

2.5 Maintain a healthy respect for the personal growth of students and provide appropriate professional referrals.

2.6 Maintain appropriate confidentiality regarding all information and knowledge gained in the course of supervision .

3.0 Ethical Principles in Relationships with Social Institutions

Spiritual Care Professionals are accountable to their faith communities, one another and other organizations. Spiritual Care Professionals:

3.1 Maintain good standing in their faith group.

3.2 Abide by the professional practice and/or teaching standards of the state/province, the community and the institution in which they are employed. If for any reason a Spiritual Care Professional is not free to practice or teach according to conscience, the Spiritual Care Professional shall notify the employer, his or her professional organization and faith group as appropriate.

3.3 Do not directly or by implication claim professional qualifications that exceed actual qualifications or misrepresent an affiliation with any institution.

4.0 Ethical Principles in Relationships with Other Professionals and the Community

Spiritual Care Professionals are accountable to the public, faith communities, employers and professionals in all professional relationships. Spiritual Care Professionals:

4.1 Promote justice in relationships with others, in their institutions and in society.

4.2 Represent accurately their professional qualifications and affiliations.

4.3 Exercise good stewardship of resources entrusted to their care and employ sound financial practices.

4.4 Respect the opinions, beliefs and professional endeavors of colleagues and other professionals.

4.5 Seek advice and counsel of other professionals whenever it is in the best interest of those being served and make referrals when appropriate.

4.6 Provide expertise and counsel to other health professionals in advocating for best practices in care.

4.7 Seek to establish collaborative relationships with other community and health professionals.

4.8 Advocate for changes in their institutions that would honor spiritual values and promote healing.

4.9 Provide other professionals with chart notes where they are used that further the treatment of the clients or patients, obtaining consent when required.

4.10 Communicate sufficient information to other care team members while respecting the privacy of clients.

4.11 Ensure that private conduct does not impair the ability to fulfill professional responsibilities or bring dishonor to the profession.

4.12 Clearly distinguish between statements made or actions taken as a private individual and those made as a member or representative of one of the cognate organizations.

5.0 Ethical Principles in Relationships with Colleagues

Spiritual Care Professionals engage in collegial relationships with peers, other chaplains, local clergy and counselors, recognizing that perspective and judgment are maintained through consultative interactions rather than through isolation. Spiritual Care Professionals:

5.1 Honor all consultations, whether personal or client–related, with the highest professional regard and confidentiality.

5.2 Maintain sensitivity and professional protocol of the employing institution and/or the certifying organization when receiving or initiating referrals.

5.3 Exercise due caution when communicating through the internet or other electronic means.

5.4 Respect each other and support the integrity and well being of their colleagues.

5.5 Take collegial and responsible action when concerns about or direct knowledge of incompetence, impairment, misconduct or violations against
this code arise.

5.6 Communicate sufficient information to other care team members while respecting the privacy of clients.

6.0 Ethical Principles in Advertising

Spiritual Care Professionals engage in appropriate informational activities that educate the public about their professional qualifications and individual scopes of practice. Spiritual Care Professionals:

6.1 Represent their competencies, education, training and experience relevant to their practice of pastoral care, education and counseling in an accurate
manner.

6.2 Do not use any professional identification (business cards, letterhead, Internet or telephone directory, etc.) if it is false, misleading, fraudulent or deceptive.

6.3 List and claim as evidence only degrees and certifications that are earned from educational institutions and/or training programs recognized by the certifying organizations of Spiritual Care Professionals.

6.4 Ascertain that the qualifications of their employees, supervisees and students are represented in a manner that is not false, misleading, fraudulent or deceptive.

6.5 Represent themselves as providing specialized services only if they have the appropriate education, training or supervised experience.

7.0 Ethical Principles in Research

Spiritual Care Professionals engaging in research follow guidelines and applicable laws that strive to protect the dignity, privacy and well-being of all participants. Spiritual Care Professionals:

7.1 Engage only in research within the boundaries of their competence.

7.2 In research activities involving human participants, are aware of and ensure that the research question, design and implementation are in full compliance with ethical principles.

7.3 Adhere to informed consent, including a clear and understandable explanation of the procedures, a description of the risks and benefits, and the duration of the desired participation.

7.4 Inform all participants of the right to withdraw consent and to discontinue involvement at any time.

7.5 Engage in research while being sensitive to the cultural characteristics of participants.

7.6 Maintain the confidentiality of all research participants and inform participants of any limits of that confidentiality.

7.7 Use any information obtained through research for professional purposes only.

7.8 Exercise conscientiousness in attributing sources in their research and writing thereby avoiding plagiarism.

7.9 Report research data and findings accurately.

8.0 Ethical Principles in Relationship to CASC/ACSS

Spiritual Care Professionals within CASC/ACSS maintain the highest possible standards of trust in relationship to one another in the interest of the public whom they serve. Spiritual Care Professionals:

8.1 Will disclose to the Chair of the National Ethics Committee, if they have been criminally charged or hold a conviction on record of an indict-able offence found within the Criminal Code of Canada and/or Narcotic statutes of Canada, or equivalent legislation in a foreign jurisdiction.

Code of Ethics of the Association of Professional Chaplains[6]

100 Code of Ethics (Description and Aspirations of APC)

The Association of Professional Chaplains is an association of providers of pastoral care endorsed by faith groups to serve persons in physical, mental, spiritual, or social need in diverse settings. The mission of the Association is to provide excellence in pastoral care and counseling through the Association's various programs and activities and to promote public support for skilled spiritual care.

The vision of the Association is to integrate professional pastoral and skilled spiritual care into the total care provided to persons in diverse settings. We seek to fulfill our vision in partnership with other organiza-tions that share our mission.

In promoting the Mission of the Association, certain principles and values undergird all organizational efforts. The Association sets forth this Code to inform its members and those with whom they work of those principles and values and the expectations for ethical behavior they engender. This Code does not undertake to define standards of profes-sional conduct of members for purposes of civil liability. In becoming a member of the Association, one affirms this Code and holds oneself accountable to it.

Membership implies agreement to participate with integrity in any process of the Association to hold oneself or other members account-able to this Code, and to accept the Standards and judgments of the Association.

110 General Principles and Values

110.1 The Association and its Members shall demonstrate commitment to these values in relationships with members, those served, colleagues

---

[6] APC website: http://www.professionalchaplains.org; info@professionalchaplains.org

and through conduct in their professional roles.

110.11 The individual person possesses dignity and worth.

110.12 The spiritual dimension of a person is an essential part of an individual's striving for health, wholeness and meaning in life.

110.13 The spiritual care of persons is a critical aspect of the total care offered in the delivery of care for public and private institutions and organizations.

110.14 Inclusivity and diversity are foundational values in pastoral services offered to persons and are valued throughout the structures of the Association.

110.15 Public advocacy related to spiritual values and social justice concerns is promoted on behalf of persons in need.

120 Ethical Standards for the Association

120.1 The Association shall promote integrity, competence, respect for the dignity of all persons, and collegiality among its members.

120.11 The Association shall admit to membership, employ and serve all qualified persons without discrimination regardless of race, ethnicity, sexual orientation, gender, age, disability, religion, or faith group.

120.12 The Association shall work for the improvement and growth of pastoral care according to its mission.

120.13 The Association shall, in conformity to its by-laws, provide structures and resources to maintain its Standards and promote its educational programs.

120.14 The Association shall follow its by-laws, policies, and processes in holding itself and its members accountable to its standards for competency and ethical behavior.

130 Ethical Standards for Members

130.1 Members shall treat all persons with dignity and respect.

130.11 Members shall serve all persons without discrimination regardless of religion, faith group, race, ethnicity, sexual orientation, gender, age, or disability.

130.12 Members shall demonstrate respect for the opinions, beliefs and professional endeavors of other members, their colleagues and those with whom they have contact in their professional role as chaplain.

130.13 Members shall affirm the religious and spiritual freedom of all persons and refrain from imposing doctrinal positions or spiritual practices on persons whom they encounter in their professional role as chaplain.

130.14 Members shall not condone or support unlawful discrimination against colleagues or others with whom they have contact in their professional role as chaplain.

130.15 Members shall be accountable for maintaining the integrity of the pastoral relationship.

They will not use their professional position with, or knowledge of, another for personal gain. They shall refrain from emotional, financial, sexual or any other form of exploitation.

130.16 Members shall not engage in sexual misconduct. Sexual misconduct includes sexual abuse, sexual exploitation and sexual harassment. Sexual misconduct includes, but is not limited to: sexual advances; requests for sexual favors; verbal, physical or visual conduct of a sexual nature; any pattern of behavior that would be perceived as sexual misconduct.

130.2 Members shall respect the privacy of all persons.

130.21 Members shall follow the policies of their employing institution regarding patient confidentiality sharing private information about those whom they serve only according to those policies, the member's religious tradition, or as required by law.

130.22 Members shall refrain from relating experiences that expose the vulnerabilities of those served or their families to derision or ridicule.

130.23 Members shall seek to guard the identities of those served in any consultations, presentations or publications unless the person served, or their family if the person cannot give consent, has given the member written permission for disclosure of the relationship.

130.24 Members shall respect the private communications of colleagues unless to do so would violate the safety and well-being of another or be in conflict with the laws or policies of the state, an institution or the Association.

130.3 Members shall conduct themselves with integrity in all their professional relationships including those whom they serve, their colleagues and the Association.

130.31 Members shall accurately represent their professional qualifications and affiliations.

130.32 Members shall maintain accurately and currently any patient records, financial accounts or other documents required in the course of their work.

130.33 Members shall respond with honesty and timeliness to any commission or representative of the Association duly authorized to make inquiry into their work.

130.34 Members shall provide the Association immediate notice of any complaint of unethical conduct made against them in a civil, criminal, ecclesiastical, employment or another professional organization's forum. Members will provide the APC Ethics Commission, or designee, in a timely fashion the information they request regarding the investigation, adjudication, dismissal or settlement of such complaint. Failure to report or provide accurate, full and truthful information constitutes a violation of this Code. A finding of unethical conduct in one of these forums may lead to discipline within APC even if the event did not occur within the scope of the member's professional role as a chaplain or a situation over which APC would have jurisdiction.

130.4 Members shall conform to the Association's expectations of competency.

130.41 Members shall maintain an active relationship and good standing within the faith communities in which they are ordained, or commissioned or endorsed.

130.42 Members shall pursue ongoing personal growth and professional development in theology, spirituality, pastoral skills, and other areas which enhance their professional proficiency.

130.43 Members shall make referrals or obtain consultations when in the best interests of those served and maintain interdisciplinary and interprofessional relationships to foster these practices.

130.44 Members shall take responsible action when they become aware that they themselves or another member is impaired or otherwise unable to maintain the Association's Code of Ethics or Standards of professional competency.

130.5 Members shall conform to the Association's expectations of professional behavior.

130.51 Members shall endeavor to enrich the mission and presence of the religious communities with which they work and are affiliated.

130.52 Members shall seek to represent the best interests of those whom they serve giving voice to the vulnerable whenever possible.

130.53 Members shall not knowingly use or permit others to use the member's services to secure unfair personal or professional advantage.

130.54 Members shall establish and maintain interprofessional relationships to foster partnerships and interdisciplinary cooperation.

Two resources for interfaith spiritual care

Leah Dawn Bueckert and Daniel S. Schipani

The first part of this appendix consists in the presentation of a model of spiritual assessment. The second part introduces the readers to a four-dimensional framework for analysis of interfaith situations. We designed these instruments in the midst of our work of caregiving and reflection on practice, and in dialogue with other colleagues in the field.

A Model of Spiritual Assessment

Spiritual assessment, or diagnosis,[1] has an essential place in guiding and evaluating caregiving practice. According to George Fitchett, the importance of spiritual assessment can be appreciated in terms of its sevenfold foundational role; it is foundational for: action (it helps to set goals for our ministry of care); communication (the conversation between caregiver and care receiver makes significant knowledge, or "dia-gnosis", possible); contracting (it leads to agreement regarding a plan of action); evaluation (it helps determine the presence or absence of desired outcomes); accountability (it provides a basis for mutual accountability and for holding caregivers professionally accountable in light of the evaluation of results); quality assurance (it is key for meeting institutional and legal expectations of professional excellence); research (it supplies data necessary to evaluate

---

[1] Some authors, such as George Fitchett, don't make distinctions between the terms *assessment* and *diagnosis*; see Fitchett's widely used book, *Assessing Spiritual Needs: A Guide for Caregivers* (Minneapolis: Fortress Press, 1993) pp. 17-20. Others, such as Nancy J. Ramsay continue to prefer the term *diagnosis* whose etymology better suggests the kind of clinical knowing that emerges between caregiver and care receiver and involves not only information gathering and interpreting but discernment as well. See *Pastoral Diagnosis: A Resource for Ministers of Care and Counseling* (Minneapolis: Fortress Press, 1998). Ramsay defines diagnosis as "an evaluative process of discerning the cause of another's difficulty in order to provide an appropriate and restorative response... Diagnosis is the practice of strategic knowledge in the sense that how a situation is named has everything to do with the interventions one develops in order to respond...'pastoral diagnosis' is understood as attending to the religious significance of experience." (pp. 1-2).

and improve both theory and practice). Further, Fitchett asserts that assessment is the touchstone of the caregivers' professional identity,[2] a key notion that he adopts from Paul Pruyser's significant contribution.[3]

All the chapters in this book include assessment considerations in more or less systematic ways.[4] The following two-level assessment model draws in part from a model designed for the field of counseling and psychotherapy.[5] It is intended as a practical resource for use by spiritual caregivers in the hospital setting.[6] Level I is useful for initial or one-time visits, and level II is applicable when there are opportunities for follow-up visits. The model is meant not merely to gather relevant information leading to meaningful analysis and interpretation; its purpose is to foster the kind of conversation that makes "diagnosis" and spiritual discernment possible. Evaluative comments about the model are found below.

---

[2] Fitchett, *Assessing Spiritual Needs*, pp. 20-22.

[3] Paul Pruyser, *The Minister as a Diagnostician: Personal Problems in Pastoral Perspective* (Philadelphia: Westminster Press, 1976), pp. 21-29. Pruyser's thesis is that "pastors, like all other professional workers, possess a body of theoretical and practical knowledge that is uniquely their own, evolved over years of practice by themselves and their forbears. Adding different bits of knowledge and techniques by borrowing from other disciplines, such as psychiatry and psychology, dos not undo the integrity and usefulness of their own basic and applied sciences. Adding clinical insights and skills to their pastoral work does not –should not—shake the authenticity of their pastoral outlook and performance." (p. 10)

[4] The most systematic and complete discussion and illustration of spiritual assessment is found in Anke Flohr's essay, "Competencies for Pastoral Work in Multicultural and Multifaith Societies", chapter 11 of this book.

[5] See P. Scott Richards and Allen E. Bergin, *A Spiritual Strategy for Counseling and Psychotherapy*, 2nd. ed. (Washington, D.C.: American Psychological Association, 2005), chapter 8, "Religious and Spiritual Assessment" (pp. 219-249). Interestingly, following the pioneering work of Richards and Bergin (first edition published in 1997), other authors have more recently stressed the significance of spirituality, and spiritual assessment in particular, in the field of counseling and psychotherapy, with the significant endorsement of the American Psychological Association; see, for example, William R. Miller, ed., *Integrating Spirituality into Treatment: Resources for Practitioners* (Washington, D.C.: American Psychological Association, 1999), chapter 3, "Assessing Spirituality" (pp. 47-64); Jamie D. Aten and Mark M. Leach, *Spirituality and the Therapeutic Process: A Comprehensive Resource from Intake to Termination* (Washington, D.C.: American Psychological Association, 2009), chapters 4—"Noting the Importance of Spirituality During Clinical Intake"—and 5—"Clinical Assessment of Clients' Spirituality" (pp. 75-120); and Thomas G. Plante, *Spiritual Practices in Psychotherapy: Thirteen Tools for Enhancing Psychological Health* (Washington, D.C.: 2009), chapter 3, "Assessment Issues" (pp. 47-64). These authors also discuss ways to actively engage care receivers' spirituality in the process of treatment following assessment or diagnosis (in which the spirituality dimension is given special attention).

[6] Clinical Pastoral Education and caregiving experience, in addition to the contributions of Richards and Bergin, and Fitchett, determine relevant dimensions of the model (Physical, Psychological, Emotional, Social, Spiritual, Educational/Occupational, Behavioral). Some of the "explicit questions" on the left of the chart are offered as examples of questions to be pondered by care receivers rather than as a questionnaire requiring specific responses.

Level I

To be used during initial visits

Explicit questions	Assessing these areas	Particular dimensions
What has your experience in the hospital been like so far?	Medical condition, level of physical discomfort, level of adjustment to hospital environment and loss of privacy, dynamics of interaction with hospital staff, level of current satisfaction with medical care, sense of psychological/emotional well-being	Physical Psychological, Emotional, Social Behavioral
Are you part of a religious community?	Person's identity as religious (particular tradition), spiritual, non-religious, agnostic, atheist; significance of participation in faith community; health of religious involvement; existence of community support network	Spiritual Ethnic/Cultural Social
Would you like me to contact your minister [or someone else from your church] to let her/him know that you are here?	Connection with people Able to receive care and comfort	Psychological Spiritual
Have your family been here to see you?	Sense of support and connection	Psychological, Emotional, Social
Do you find prayer helpful?	Likelihood that person's faith will be a source of strength and comfort or a hindrance, sense of hope, presence of spiritual/religious concerns, and needs, images/experiences of God, sense of meaning/purpose	Spiritual
May I pray with you?	Does the person welcome the spiritual caregiver's prayer?	Spiritual

LEVEL II

To be used during follow-up visits

Explicit questions[a]	Assessing these areas	Particular dimensions
Last time we talked you mentioned..., how are you feeling about that today?	How the person is progressing through his/her experience	Psychological/ Emotional
Are there things that help distract you to make it more tolerable?*[b]	Ability to cope, sources of strength and encouragement	Psychological/ Emotional
What brings you the most joy and satisfaction in life?	Sense of meaning and purpose, level of gratitude or dissatisfaction, significant relationships	Psychological/ Emotional Spiritual
What do you look forward to doing when you return home?	Person's vocational involvements, sense of hope	Educational/ Occupational
How do you think your life might change as a result of this experience?	Level of reflection on implications of illness or accident, sense of loss/grief, sense of hope, support resources	Psychological/ Emotional Physical
Have you had any thoughts about God lately?*	Reflections about the experience in light of person's faith, images of God, childhood religious affiliation	Spiritual
What does dying mean for you?*	Fears, hopes, losses, views about life beyond death, last wishes	Spiritual Psychological/ Emotional Physical

Continued ...

[a] The questions asked during a follow-up visit depend, obviously, on the person's particular situation. If a patient experiences an extended hospital stay, some of the reasons a spiritual caregiver might make a follow-up visit include: if the patient undergoes stressful treatment or expresses stress regarding impending lifestyle changes, if the patient has expressed spiritual concerns or needs, if the nursing staff specifically request follow-up with a particular patient, if the person is dying, if the person is relatively isolated with few friends and family around, and so on.

[b] Questions followed by an asterisk come from Clair Hochstetler, "Pastoral Ministers and Volunteers: Qualifications, Training, and Functions," in *Spiritual Caregiving in the Hospital: Windows to Chaplaincy Ministry*, edited by Leah Dawn Bueckert and Daniel S. Schipani (Kitchener: Pandora Press, 2006) pp. 71-72.

Explicit questions	Assessing these areas	Particular dimensions
Are there things you would like to say to anyone that you haven't had a chance to say?*	Health of interpersonal relation-ships, communication needs, feelings of anger, remorse, fear, love	Psychological/ Emotional Social Spiritual
How can we best support you during these days?*	Person's sense of her/his main concerns and needs	Pyschological/ Emotional

Evaluation of the Assessment Model

George Fitchett's text includes a number of guidelines and criteria for evaluating models of spiritual assessment.[7] The following evaluative comments on the model presented here are an application of those guidelines.

Concepts about the spiritual aspects of life

Specific questions and the number of questions that can be asked in the initial assessment process will of course vary according to the situation and length of time available. During initial spiritual care visits in the hospital, spiritual caregivers gather information both directly and indirectly. They draw from both the explicit and implicit expressions of the person's experience. The hope is to establish rapport with patients in such a way that they are able to communicate freely about their concerns, questions, needs, and sources of support. The personal demeanor of the spiritual caregiver is, therefore, as important as the technique of assessment or more. In the words of James Michael Lewis: "A patient subjected to the staff's medically necessary intrusions may actually relish the visit of a chaplain who approaches him or her as a person rather than an object for clinical examination."[8] (It is also the case, of course, that many nurses and other medical staff provide care that puts human dignity first).

This assessment model includes both questions that are open-ended (such as, "What has your experience in the hospital been like so far?") and closed-ended (for example, "Would you like me to contact your minister?"). The closed-ended questions are for the purpose of gathering specific information. With the open-ended questions spiritual caregivers

[7] Fitchett, *Assessing Spiritual Needs*, pp. 90-104.
[8] James Michael Lewis, "Pastoral Assessment in Hospital Ministry: A Conversational Approach", *Chaplaincy Today*, 18:2 (Autumn/Winter 2002), p. 6.

are also listening for specific information, but the tone with which patients respond and the choices they make about what to share and what not to share are as important as the actual content of their response. During an initial visit, questions are geared toward a general understanding of the person's spirituality. If there is a follow-up visit, the caregiver may ask more specifically and directly about a patient's thoughts about God, for example.

The model is substantive and functional. It addresses both what the person believes and values as well as the ways in which they express or are influenced by these beliefs and values.

It is common for patients and hospital staff to assume that spiritual caregivers focus solely on the spiritual dimension of patients' experience. Actually, they are interested not only in spirituality narrowly viewed, but especially in the ways in which the person's physical experience affects their psychological, emotional, spiritual, social well-being and so on and vice versa. This addresses questions about the holistic context of the model. There are (at least) seven dimensions to be assessed as part of this model, in no particular order: physical, psychological/emotional, social, spiritual, ethnic/cultural, behavioral, and educational/occupational. On the one hand, the spiritual dimension is one of the seven and can be distinguished in significant ways from the other dimensions. On the other hand, because of the caregiver's spiritual care perspective, the model also suggests that the definition of spiritual care is precisely the holding together of all facets of human experience, essentially interconnected as they are.

This model is limited in its use as a developmental model over time as it is intended for one-time interactions. Of course, if there is opportunity to move to level II, dynamics of change and growth are most definitely potential areas of assessment.

Congruency between what patients say and how they live is explored to some extent. Questions about involvement in religious communities, prayer, and current sources of support may reveal some of these dynamics.

Norms and authority

The question, "Do you participate in a religious community?" often elicits a sheepish response if the person thinks they should attend church and don't. The reason for asking that question, however, is to determine whether or not that kind of activity is meaningful for the person. The spiritual norm implied in this model is that everyone needs some kind of sense of belonging, meaning, and community support, whether that comes through a religious community or some other type of group or network. In light of this, signs of spiritual health or pathology that are assessed with this tool include determining whether the person has a community and feels nurtured by it, has a community and feels oppressed by it, or does not have such a community, to name some of the possibilities.

The model is oriented toward growth as the questions encourage patients to do some of the work of integrating their condition with their lifestyle and values. A spiritual caregiver may also glean insight about dysfunction to the extent that there is opportunity for patients to share, whether intentionally or unintentionally, about their struggles,

Both patient and caregiver are active parties in the assessment process, with the balance varying according to personality styles, the patient's physical (or other) condition, and so on.

Context and process

This model for spiritual care assessment in the hospital is carried out in the manner of informational yet intentional conversation with patients. It is geared toward the development of a clinical spiritual care plan. This model would be used by spiritual caregivers who have had at least some measure of training, either Clinical Pastoral Education, social work, or counseling. It may also be used by pastoral volunteers who have received workshop style training in responsive listening, asking good questions, respecting worldviews of others, confidentiality, and so on. Level I of the assessment model may be carried out in a fifteen-minute conversation with a patient, followed by appropriate charting, consultation with other hospital staff, and the development of a spiritual care plan, if necessary. As far as initial visits are concerned, fifteen minutes is usually what is both available and recommended because of patients' limited tolerance for extended conversation as well as the spiritual caregiver's goal of making connection with a number of patients. Using Level II of the model is less defined in terms of time, depending on the length of a patient's stay at the hospital and the intensity of their experience.

Application of assessment model to an experience with "John"

The following account comes from a real-life caregiving situation. It is meant only as an illustration of how the assessment model can be employed in the flow of the interaction between care giver and care receiver whether or not such interaction is defined as "interfaith", which happens not to be the case in this instance.

John was a 70-year-old patient whom I (Leah Dawn) met on a post-surgical unit of the hospital where I was serving as chaplain intern. He had come in for back surgery but then ended up staying for an extended period of time because of complications. During my first visit with John and his wife Anita, John was quiet but hopeful about recovery. I learned that they are part of a Mennonite church, that John had been very instrumental in the youth program, and that their minister had come to visit. There were cards, photos, and drawings from grandchildren on the bulletin board. After our conversation, they welcomed my praying with them. Because they seemed to have sufficient support, at that point I decided that this initial visit would likely be the only visit I made to John and Anita.

Over the next few weeks, however, it became clear that there were complications cropping up in relation to the surgery and I visited John (sometimes with Anita, sometimes not) several more times. I no longer remember the exact nature of the complications, but John became more and more depressed as time went on and he did not seem to improve. He was often very non-responsive to my questions, but always seemed open to prayer. I learned that he liked to listen to books on tape to pass the time. At the beginning he spoke about the satisfaction he experienced in being with his family and his grandchildren, but gradually his comments became more and more apathetic and hopeless. I asked many questions like those listed on the Level II assessment and more. The psychologist on the care team was prescribing anti-depressants for him. Anita was growing more anxious and agitated as the weeks went by.

In light of this, my care plan followed along the lines of "pastoral care actions" as described by Lewis[9] and others: To be an encouraging pastoral presence—I communicated appreciation of his existential struggles, affirmed his wrestling with God, and often sat quietly with him for a period of time. I did not perform any religious sacraments or rituals in this situation. I did, however, read scripture. I also found, in the seminary library, a cassette tape series with Richard Rohr's reflections on the book of Job. John listened to these and we talked about the story in relation to his own experience, which involved a kind of pastoral counseling. I offered spontaneous intercessory prayer each time we met which John clearly and consistently appreciated.

John did eventually return home. His depression did not really seem

---

[9] Ibid.,p. 12. Another helpful resource on assessment and pastoral action is Arthur M. Lucas, "Introduction to *The Discipline* for Pastoral Care Giving," in Larry VandeCreek and Arthur M. Lucas, eds., *The Discipline for Pastoral Care Giving: Foundations for Outcome Oriented Chaplaincy* (New York: Haworth Pastoral Press, 2001.The contribution of this approach consists in its focus on desirable outcomes that stem from assessing the care receiver's needs, hopes and resources; those desirable outcomes determine the plan of action, orient pastoral "interventions" (sic) and become criteria to measure the results of the caregiving process.

to lift while he was in hospital. I hope that my interactions with him, along with those of other hospital staff and family, were to some degree embodiments of hope, grace, and love in the midst of his spiritual struggle to find meaning and purpose, physical and psychological healing, and connection with significant others.

Four-dimensional framework for analysis of interfaith spiritual caregiving situations

The following instrument was created in the setting of the seminar group the editors led at Lutheran Hospital of Indiana which was briefly mentioned in the introduction of this book. It is useful for analysis and discussion of spiritual care situations for two related reasons. First of all, the inductive quality of the four-dimensional structure resembles the dynamic flow of the actual caregiving process seen from the caregiver's perspective: from assessment and understanding to discernment of desirable goals and appropriate strategy and approach and evaluation.[10] Second, the potential value of this conceptual tool resides in its structure, which is analogous to the very pattern of practical theology as a discipline.[11]

Readers are invited to review chapter 5—"A chaplain reflects on caring for a Jewish family"—and consider the situation faced by William (Bill) Griffith, a Baptist spiritual cregiver in light of the four-dimensional framework, as suggested below. They are also encouraged to add reflective observations to those supplied for each of the four dimensions—empirical, hermeneutical, normative, and strategic and pragmatic—of practical-theological analysis.

---

[10] The value of using the four-dimensional framework as a structure for reflecting and reporting on caregiving practice is clearly illustrated in Leah Dawn Bueckert's chapter, "Holistic Care as a Moral Imperative: Insights from Women's Experience of Hysterectomy and Mastectomy," in Leah Dawn Bueckert and Daniel S. Schipani, eds., *Spiritual Caregiving in the Hospital: Windows to Chaplaincy Ministry* (Kitchener: Pandora Press, 2006), pp. 219-232. The four-part essay discusses the following themes: listening to women's voices, interpreting women's experiences, identifying norms for holistic care, and reshaping caregiving practices.

[11] Practical theology is understood as a critical and constructive reflection on ministry practice broadly viewed, with special focus on formation and transformation processes such as those fostered in pastoral and spiritual care. It is a unique discipline with a fourfold nature: it is empirically grounded and contextually situated; hermeneutic in character; fundamentally normative; and pragmatically and strategically oriented. For a detailed, illustrated discussion of the four main tasks of practical theology, see Richard R. Osmer, *Practical Theology: An Introduction* (Grand Rapids: Eerdmans, 2008). Two additional helpful texts on practical theology from Christian perspectives are: Ray S. Anderson, *The Shape of Practical Theology: Empowering Ministry with Theological Praxis* (Downers Grove: InterVarsity Press, 2001), and Dorothy C. Bass and Craig Dykstra, eds., *For Life Abundant: Practical Theology, Theological Education, and Christian Ministry* (Grand Rapids: Eerdmans , 2008).

1. **OBSERVE and DESCRIBE (the *empirical* dimension) -** What do we perceive or, what is going on in this situation? What are the key issues we can identify in this interfaith encounter?

   - Bill, a Baptist chaplain meets a Jewish family during the last hours of Jacob's life

     - The chaplain is ready to either communicate with a rabbi or to offer appropriate pastoral care in their (the family's) terms

     - Jacob's wife welcomes the Christian chaplain, affirms spiritual common ground between chaplain and family, and anticipates that spiritual care will be available to them

     - Bill joins the family circle and invites those present to tell stories about Jacob and their relationship with him

     - He then affirms the expressions of love and mutual support he has witnessed

     - Bill finally asks permission to leave with the family a prayer and an Old Testament text; he also reads Psalm 23 and comments briefly on God being with us in times of distress

     - He leaves the scene with a sense of having been a caring presence to that Jewish family while also having been blessed by them

     - Key issues from a psychological perspective: a family gathering around a dying person that reflects a unique family system and culture with traits such as manifest love and communion, respect, and shared values; a sense of imminent loss and grief (perhaps including uncertainty regarding widowhood); emotional resources to cope with the death of a spouse, father, grandfather; a disposition to welcome support and extend hospitality. A competent chaplain who becomes available and activates his own psychological and clinical resourcefulness.

     - Key issues from a theological perspective: manifestations of Grace in the face of the irreversible nature of death (personally experienced by at least spiritual caregiver and spouse, and mediated among family members and by the caregiver); trust in divine care; appropriation of Scripture, prayer and blessing as spiritual gifts transcending religious boundaries.

     - Other descriptive observations…?

2. **INTERPRET (the *hermeneutical* dimension)** - Why do caregiver and care receivers act the way they do? What is the psychological and theological significance of those actions? What is the caregiver trying to accomplish or, what goals does he have in mind regarding himself and desired outcomes for the care receivers?

- Bill set for himself, as usual, a number of general goals such as these:

  ♦ To faithfully represent the healing Christ and the church as a community of wholeness and hope

  ♦ To accept (and to offer) hospitality in a caring space where care seekers could express themselves freely and receive the support they need

  ♦ To become a temporary companion in this family's journey of grief and healing

  ♦ To minister as a spiritual caregiver who interacts with the family in spiritually sensitive ways and with clinical competence

  ♦ Other interpretive remarks…?

- More specifically related to the critical episode involving Jacob, his wife and the rest of the family, Bill's objectives included the following:

  ♦ For Jacob's wife and the family, to experience validation of their grief as well as their strengths both as a family and individually

  ♦ For both the family and Bill to identify and activate available resources, internal (e.g. memories and stories, faith) and external (Scripture, other people), to help them face the painful transition

  ♦ For the family, to receive spiritual support grounded in their faith and family tradition

  ♦ Other interpretive remarks…?

3. **JUDGE (the *normative* dimension)** - What are the ethical-theological norms that seem to be at work in the situation? To what extent is the caregiver´s work effective or functional, from a psychological viewpoint, and faithful or appropriate, from a theological perspective?[12] Are there alternative norms that should be considered

---

[12] The question of psychological functionality and theological adequacy in any given spiritual care

in this particular case?

- The spiritual caregiver's ministry to the Jewish family is psychologically effective or "functional":
  - Bill prepares himself for the occasion including alternative plans and careful observation and attention with heightened awareness
  - Having been welcomed, he sensitively enters into their reality in their terms
  - He gently invites family members to tell stories that evoke pleasant memories and elicit gratitude and celebration of the dying man's life
  - He spends an optimal amount of time with the family and leaves with the assurance that his caregiving has been appreciated and that he has contributed to a meaningful grieving process
  - Other evaluative comments…?
- His caregiving is theologically appropriate:
  - He is able to minister "Christianly"[13] with integrity, that is, with due respect for the Jewish faith and tradition of the family and without compromising his own convictions
  - His Christological and soteriological beliefs don't prevent Bill from caring well for the Jewish family
  - He has an adequate understanding (and theology) of Scripture, faith, prayer, blessing, and of the continuities and discontinuities between his faith and the care receivers' faith
  - His actions (praying, blessing, reading Scripture, briefly sharing comments on the text, etc.) are also theologically appropriate
  - Other evaluative comments…?

4. **ACT (the *strategic and pragmatic* dimension)** - Can we identify some principles—understood as dependable guides to practice—for

---

situation is discussed systematically by Deborah van Deusen Hunsinger in *Theology and Pastoral Counseling: A New Interdisciplinary Approach* (Grand Rapids: Eerdmans, 1995); definitions are found on pp. 121-130.

[13] In the introduction of this book we defined the expression "caring Christianly" as the kind of spiritual care that stems from a certain vision of reality and the good life, a disposition to care as a form of love of neighbor inspired by Jesus, and a sense of vocation experienced as partnership with the Spirit of God. These dimensions of the Christian faith define the caregivers' identity and ministry.

excellence in spiritual care in light of our analysis? Or, how does our analysis illumine possible growth in professional wisdom in terms of being, knowing, and doing?

- Bill's ministry to this family illustrates a number of core competencies of being indispensable to full presence with the family:

  - A clear sense of personal and vocational identity

  - Optimal self-awareness, including a realistic view of strengths and limitations

  - A plurality of character strengths such as acceptance, respect and sensitivity; humility and compassion; freedom to be vulnerable and openness to new experiences; etc.

  - A spirituality that embraces complexity and paradox (e.g. regarding the normativeness of Jesus Christ and the truthfulness of the care receivers' non-Christian faith)

  - Other suggestions...?

- As a spiritual caregiver, Bill demonstrates the value of several core competencies of knowing essential for understanding and discernment:

  - A philosophy of caregiving primarily grounded in his Christian faith tradition and shaped by professional training and experience

  - Knowledge of the complexities, dynamics, richness and challenges of interfaith situations

  - Understanding of at least one other faith tradition different than his own

  - Clinical and theological knowing and assessment

  - Other suggestions...?

- Bill's work also illustrates core competencies of doing required for the fine art of companioning in spiritual care:

  - He relates to the Jewish family in ways that engage their emotions and their spirituality

  - He encourages and guides the family members in a time of storytelling

  - He is a participant-observer who internally monitors ongoing caregiving activity thus maximizing effectiveness while avoiding invasive or intrusive interventions

- He provides a number of responses in several caregiving modes (e.g. gently probing, supporting, praying, reading, blessing)
- Other suggestions…?

Selected bibliography

Anderson, Herbert, ed. *Reflective Practice: Formation and Supervision in Ministry*. Volume 28, 2009.

Anderson, Robert G. & Mary A. Fukuyama, eds. *Ministry in the Spiritual and Cultural Diversity of Health Care: Increasing the Competency of Chaplains*. New York: Haworth Pastoral Press, 2004.

Aten, Jamie D. and Mark M. Leach, eds. *Spirituality and the Therapeutic Process: A Comprehensive Resource from Intake to Termination*. Washington, D.C.: American Psychological Association, 2009.

Borg, Marcus J. *The Heart of Christianity: Rediscovering a Life of Faith*. New York: Harper Collins, 2003.

Bueckert, Leah Dawn & Daniel S. Schipani. *Spiritual Caregiving in the Hospital: Windows to Chaplaincy Ministry*. Kitchener: Pandora Press, 2006.

Campbell, Cynthia M. *A Multitude of Blessings: A Christian Approach to Religious Diversity*. Louisville: Westminster John Knox Press, 2007.

Dodd, Carley H. *Dynamics of Intercultural Communication*. 5th ed. Boston: McGraw Hill, 1998.

Dupuis, SJ. Jacques. *Toward a Christian Theology of Religious Pluralism*. Maryknoll: Orbis Books, 1997.

Fitchett, George. *Assessing Spiritual Needs: A Guide for Caregivers*. Minneapolis: Augsburg Fortress, 1993.

Fosarelli, Pat. *Prayers & Rituals at a Time of Illness & Dying*. West Conshohocken: Templeton Foundation Press, 2008.

Fowler, James W. *Faith Development and Pastoral Care*. Philadelphia: Fortress Press, 1987.

Fukujama, Mary A. & Todd D. Sevig. *Integrating Spirituality into Multicultural Counseling*. Thousand Oaks: Sage Publications, 1999.

Grant, Brian W. *A Theology for Pastoral Psychotherapy: God's Play in Sacred Spaces*. New York: The Haworth Pastoral Press, 2001.

Griffith, James L. & Melissa Elliott Griffith. *Encountering the Sacred in Psychotherapy: How To Talk with People about their Spiritual Lives.* New York: The Guilford Press, 2002.

Griffith, William, H. *Lessons in Care-Giving for the Dying: More than a Parting Prayer.* Valley Forge: Judson Press, 2004.

Heim, S. Mark. *The Depth of Riches: A Trinitarian Theology of Religious Ends.* Grand Rapids: Eerdmans, 2001.

Kirkwood, Neville A. *A Hospital Handbook on Multiculturalism and Religion.* Rev. ed. Harrisburg: Morehouse Publishing, 2005.

Koenig, Harold G. *Spirituality in Patient Care.* Rev. and expanded 2nd.ed. Philadelphia & London:Templeton Foundation Press, 2007.

Lewis, James Michael. "Pastoral Assessment in Hospital Ministry: A Conversational Approach," *Chaplaincy Today*, 18:2 (Autumn-Winter 2002), 5:13.

Lord, Janice Harris, Melissa Hook, Sharifa Alkhateeb, Sharon J. English. *Spiritually Sensitive Caregiving: A Multi-Faith Handbook.* Burnsville: Compassion Books, 2008.

March, W. Eugene. *The Wide, Wide Circle of Divine Love.* Louisville: Westminster John Knox Press, 2004.

Meier, Augustine, Thomas St. James O'Connor, Peter L. VanKatwyk, eds. *Spirituality & Health: Multidisciplinary Explorations.* Waterloo: Wilfrid Laurier University, 2005.

Mottran, Kenneth P. *Caring for those in Crisis: Facing Ethical Dilemmas with Patients and Families.* Grand Rapids: Brazos Press, 2007.

Netland, Harold. *Encountering Religious Pluralism: The Challenge to Christian Faith and Mission.* Downers Grove: InterVarsity Press, 2001.

Orchard, Helen, ed. *Spirituality in Health Care Contexts.* London & Philadelphia: 2001.

Paloutzian, Raymond F. & Crystal L. Park, eds. *Handbook of the Psychology of Religion and Spirituality.* New York: The Guilford Press, 2005.

Pederson, Paul B. et al. *Counseling Across Cultures.* 5th ed. Thousand Oaks: Sage Publications, 2002.

Plante, Thomas G. *Spiritual Practices in Psychotherapy: Thirteen Tools for Enhancing Psychological Health.* Washington, D.C.: American Psychological Association, 2009.

Ramsay, Nancy J. *Pastoral Diagnosis: A Resource for Ministers of Care and Counseling.* Minneapolis: Fortress Press, 1998.

Richards, P. Scott & Allen E. Bergin, eds. *Handbook of Psychotherapy and Religious Diversity.* Washington, D.C.: American Psychological Association, 2000.

Schipani, Daniel S. & Leah Dawn Bueckert, eds. *Interfaith Spiritual Care: Understandings and Practices.* Kitchener: Pandora Press, 2009.

Stairs, Jean. *Listening for the Soul: Pastoral Care and Spiritual Direction.* Minneapolis: Fortress Press, 2000.

Suchocki, Marjorie Hewitt. *Divinity & Diversity: A Christian Affirmation of Religious Pluralism.* Nashville: Abingdon Press, 2004.

Sue, Derald Wing and David Sue. *Counseling the Culturally Diverse.* 5th ed. New York: J. Wiley, 2007.

Taylor, Elizabeth Johnson. *What Do I Say?: Talking with Patients about Spirituality.* Philadelphia & London: Templeton Foundation Press, 2007.

The Otawa Hospital. DVD: *Spiritual Care in a Multi-Faith Context Series, Vol. 1: Multy-Faith Perspectives on End-of-Life Issues.* October 2005.

Toole, Mary M. *Handbook for Chaplains: Comfort my People.* New York: Paulist Press, 2006.

VandeCreek, Larry & Arthur M. Lucas, eds. *The Discipline for Pastoral Care Giving: Foundations for Outcome Oriented Chaplaincy.* New York: The Haworth Pastoral Press, 2001.

Vanier, Jean. *Befriending the Stranger.* Toronto: Novalis, 2005.

Wintz, Sue & E. Cooper. *Learning Module for Cultural and Spiritual Sensitivity,* and *Quick Guides to Cultures and Traditions,* www.professionalchaplains.org (2000).

Spiritual Caregiving in the Hospital
Windows to Chaplaincy Ministry
Revised edition

Leah Dawn Bueckert and Daniel S. Schipani, editors

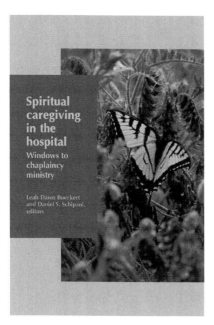

ISBN 978-1-926599-20-5
332 pages – Softcover

For ordering information contact
Pandora Press
33 Kent Avenue
Kitchener, ON
N2G 3R2

Telephone: 519.578.2381
Fax: 519.578.1826
Toll Free: 866.696.1678
E-mail: karl@pandorapress.com
Web site: www.pandorapress.com

Even as hospitals increasingly recognize spiritual care as an essential component of holistic care, chaplains are still in the process of defining their role. This book acknowledges and celebrates the unique contribution of hospital chaplains, fosters understanding and support for their work, and seeks to elicit interest in their ministry of spiritual caregiving. The writers bring together a wealth of conceptual and practical information for those engaged in the challenging ministry of caring for persons in crisis. Required reading for any chaplain or spiritual care provider, this book is also an excellent resource for those training professional caregivers.

Teresa E. Snorton,
Executive Director,
Association for Clinical
Pastoral Education

What reviewers are saying

Excerpts from professional reviews of *Spiritual Caregiving in the Hospital: Windows to Chaplaincy Ministry*

This is a wonderful anthology of practical wisdom, which both the clinical pastoral education (CPE) student and the experienced chaplain will find useful.... Have the editors met their stated goals? The answer is a resounding "yes!" Primarily, this is accomplished by the contributors who have extensive experience as practitioners of the art of chaplaincy. Chaplains thus see their ministry through the metaphor of a "clean" window, encountering each author directly and intimately through the effective use of biblical imagery, anecdotes, poetry, personal experience, and case studies. I heartily recommend this book as a required text for CPE students as well as a necessary addition to any chaplain's library.

Christian Demlow, DMin, BCC, *Chaplaincy Today*

Spiritual Caregiving in the Hospital succeeds because the book is written by reflective practitioners of the art.... Opening "windows to chaplaincy ministry" is an apt metaphor for the editors' intention to allow a better view of healthcare chaplaincy by getting out of the reader's way.... I commend a thorough reading of this book by chaplains, students and teachers of pastoral care—anyone interested in this vital discipline!

Phil Pinckard, MDiv, BCC, *PlainViews*

Spiritual Caregiving in the Hospital has many strengths. The underlying theology woven into every chapter is incarnational spiritual care.... Each chapter is full of case studies, dialogues between patients and chaplains, and clinical vignettes. These are necessary components of pastoral theology. The ministry of these chaplains is quite impressive given the challenging situations that many share. Throughout the chapters, spiritual and theological reflections are integrated into spiritual care like threads of a tapestry. One has a sense that theological reflection is essential to these chaplains' praxis. There is plenty of variety in this book and the definition of spirituality outlined is inclusive and interfaith.... This book is a resource for ministry.... I plan to use this text in my Clinical Pastoral Education units and in my graduate course on Spirituality and Health.

Thomas St. James O'Connor, ThD, CPE Supervisor, *The Journal of Pastoral Care and Counseling*

Leah Dawn Bueckert, MDiv in pastoral care and counseling (Associated Mennonite Biblical Seminary), serves as spiritual care coordinator with the North Eastman Health Association in Manitoba, Canada. She is based in the community of Beausejour.

Daniel S. Schipani, PsyD (Universidad Católica Argentina), PhD (Princeton Theological Seminary), is professor of pastoral care and counseling at Associated Mennonite Biblical Seminary, located in Elkhart, Indiana.

Interfaith Spiritual Care
Understandings and practices

Daniel S. Schipani, and Leah Dawn Bueckert, editors

ISBN 978-1-926599-07-6
322 pages – Softcover

For ordering information contact
Pandora Press
33 Kent Avenue
Kitchener, ON
N2G 3R2

Telephone: 519.578.2381
Fax: 519.578.1826
Toll Free: 866.696.1678
E-mail: karl@pandorapress.com
Web site: www.pandorapress.com

The twofold overarching concern of the project leading to this publication is to foster reflection and enhance the practice of interfaith spiritual care in health care institutions and beyond. Endorsed by the Society for Intercultural Pastoral Care and Counseling, the book meets the following goals:

- to explore the dynamics of interfaith spiritual care as a work of practical and pastoral theology;

- to identify reliable guidelines for competent practice and duly contextualized interfaith spiritual care;

- to invite further conversation and collaboration among practitioners and scholars.

This book is intended for chaplains, pastors, Clinical Pastoral Education students, and other caregivers such as counselors adn psychotherapists, both in training and already in practice.